ROOFS OF GOLD

Poems to Read Aloud

EDITED AND WITH AN INTRODUCTION

By PADRAIC COLUM

THE MACMILLAN COMPANY, NEW YORK

COLLIER-MACMILLAN LIMITED, LONDON

821.8 C72r
In83   c. 1

To my young friends
Charles and Thomas Crane

Copyright © Padraic Colum 1964. All rights reserved. No part of this book may be reproduced or utilized in any form or by any means, electronic or mechanical, including photocopying, recording or by any information storage and retrieval system, without permission in writing from the Publisher. First Printing. Library of Congress catalog card number: 64-23076. The Macmillan Company, New York. Collier-Macmillan Canada, Ltd., Toronto, Ontario. Designed by Hilda Scott. Printed in the United States of America.

ACKNOWLEDGMENTS

We wish to thank the following publishers and authors' representatives for permission to reprint the following selections:

Curtis Brown Ltd., London, on behalf of the Roy Campbell Estate for "Tristan da Cunha." Jonathan Cape Ltd. and Holt, Rinehart & Winston, Inc., Proprietors for "After Apple-Picking" from *The Complete Poems of Robert Frost*. Coward-McCann, Inc., and Herbert Jenkins Ltd., London, for "To a Linnet in a Cage" from *The Complete Poems of Francis Ledwidge*. The Executors of the Dylan Thomas Estate and J. M. Dent & Sons Ltd., for "Fern Hill." Faber and Faber Ltd., London, for "little tree" by e. e. cummings: *Selected Poems;* "Growltiger's Last Stand" by T. S. Eliot: *Old Possum's Book of Practical Cats;* "The Express" by Stephen Spender: *Col-*

NOV '64
W I

lected Poems. Harcourt, Brace & World, Inc., for "Growltiger's Last Stand" from Old Possum's Book of Practical Cats, copyright, 1939, by T. S. Eliot; "little tree" from Poems 1923–1954, copyright 1925, 1953, by e. e. cummings. Holt, Rinehart and Winston, Inc., for "After Apple-Picking" from Complete Poems of Robert Frost, copyright 1930, 1939 by Holt, Rinehart and Winston, Inc.; "The Oracles" from Complete Poems by A. E. Housman, copyright 1922 by Holt, Rinehart and Winston, Inc., copyright renewed 1950 by Barclays Bank Ltd. Donagh MacDonagh for Thomas MacDonagh's "The Night Hunt." Macmillan & Company, Ltd., London, for "The Parrots" from The Collected Poems of W. W. Gibson. The Macmillan Company of Canada Limited for "The Darkling Thrush" from Collected Poems of Thomas Hardy, also by permission of the Trustees of the Hardy Estate and Macmillan & Company, Ltd., London; "Danny Murphy," "In the Orchard," and "Seumas Beg" from Collected Poems by James Stephens, also by permission of Mrs. Iris Wise, and Macmillan & Company, Ltd., London. The Macmillan Company for "The Puppet Play," "Spider," "The Wall of China," and "The Wind" copyright 1964, by Padraic Colum; "The Darkling Thrush" from Collected Poems of Thomas Hardy, copyright 1925 by The Macmillan Company; "The Broncho That Would Not Be Broken" from Collected Poems by Vachel Lindsay, copyright 1917 by The Macmillan Company, renewed 1945 by Elizabeth C. Lindsay; "Cargoes" from Poems by John Masefield, copyright 1912 by The Macmillan Company, renewed 1940 by John Masefield; from Collected Poems by James Stephens: "Danny Murphy" (copyright 1912 by The Macmillan Company, renewed 1940 by James Stephens), "In the Orchard" (copyright 1915 by The Macmillan Company, renewed 1943 by James Stephens), and "Seumas Beg" (copyright 1909 by The Macmillan Company); from The Collected Poems of W. B. Yeats: "The Cat and the Moon" (copyright 1919 by The Macmillan Company, renewed 1946 by Bertha Georgie Yeats) and "The Lake Isle of Innisfree" (copyright 1906 by The Macmillan Company, renewed 1934 by William B. Yeats). Monica McCall, Inc., for "Boy with His Hair Cut Short," copyright 1938 by Muriel Rukeyser. New Directions, Publishers, for "Boy with His Hair Cut Short" from Selected Poems of Muriel Rukeyser, copyright 1951 by Muriel Rukeyser; "Fern Hill" from The Collected Poems of Dylan Thomas, copyright 1953 by Dylan Thomas, copyright 1957 by New Directions. Random House, Inc., for "The Express" from Collected Poems 1928–1953 by Stephen Spender, copyright 1934 and renewed 1961 by Stephen Spender. Martin Secker and Warburg Limited, Publishers, for "The Old Ships" by James Elroy Flecker. The Society of Authors for "The Oracles" by A. E. Housman, also by permission of the Estate of the late A. E. Housman and Messrs. Jonathan Cape Ltd., publishers of A. E. Housman's Collected Poems.

We are indebted to Dover Publications, Inc., for the use of woodcuts by Thomas Bewick. The illustration in the Introduction was drawn by H. Lawrence Hoffman.

INTRODUCTION

The illustration in the newspaper that has come to me today shows the figures of three women. In one the hair is flowing over her shoulders. In another it is arranged around her head. In the third a crown is over it. They wear necklaces, too. Statues, you might say when you looked at the illustration. You would be nearly right: statues they are, wooden statues, figureheads that were carved on the fronts of sailing ships. Always they were looking in the direction in which the ships were sailing—that is why they have that watching expression. I imagine their dresses were colored—blue, white, yellow. Now the ships they guided are broken up, and the figures are in a museum.

As I am writing about poetry, it is odd, you might think, that I begin by mentioning figureheads. The reason is that under their pictures there is an old ballad. It is about a ship.

I imagine that the man who made the ballad and the man who carved the figureheads and gave them their bright colors would enjoy talking with each other. The man who made the ballad might think it was grand to carve the figures that looked alive and added so much beauty to the ships. But he believed, too, that he had an advantage over the carver. When the one who admired them went away he couldn't take the figureheads along—he could take only the memory of them. The ballad he could learn by heart, and, wherever he went, he could say it to himself. The ballad wouldn't have colors, but it would have music, lines of equal length that rhymed with each other, making a charm that matched the charm of color.

Near the little seaside town in Ireland where there is the museum that has the figureheads, an old man who lived by himself knew the ballad by heart. A little girl used to go see him, sweep his floor for him, wash his plates and cups and saucers, and bring him water from the well. He used to sing the ballad to her. It was a long ballad, eighteen or twenty verses, and it was about a ship that was nearly lost in a wrecking sea. The little girl wanted to know it from first verse to last, so that she could sing it or say it to herself when there was no one with her. Well, the old man made a bargain: he would teach it all to her, verse by verse, a verse for every pail of water she would carry from the well into the house.

It was a nice arrangement. I can think of the little girl taking the pail from the corner and crossing a field to the well, changing the weight of the pail from one hand to the other as she came back. Maybe there would be a bird singing in the hedge, a blackbird or a redbreast. Then she would sit by the hearth fire with the old man—I think he had been a ship's captain—and learn a verse

while the crickets chirruped in the ashes. She must have thought she had done well for herself when she had the whole ballad. It kept its treasureableness for her through all the changes of a lifetime. I expect she was as old as the one who gave it to her when she wrote the ballad down and gave it to go beside the figureheads in the little museum.

There are two things I like about this little history. The youngster learned it because she thought it was a grand thing to know the ballad, and it remained a grand thing for her through her lifetime. And—this is important—she earned something that she wanted to keep.

Now somebody may think I have made a mistake in the last sentence—"earned" should be "learned"? If you consider, you will come to know that "earned" is not wrong when it comes to speaking about the possession of poetry. For why do we get excited about a poem (or a picture or a tune)? It is because it opens a prospect to us that is brighter, braver, or even more mournful than what is around us:

> Toll for the brave!
> The brave that are no more.

The words come to us, and it is as if some voice that knows more than we know, more than anybody around us can know, is telling us about a happening that has deprived us of persons we could have admired and loved. And when we hear it said:

> On Linden, when the sun was low,
> All bloodless lay the untrodden snow,
> And dark as winter was the flow
> Of Iser, rolling rapidly.

we know of a river more dark, a covering more snowy, a sun lower than any we have ever seen, because the poet, by using the words "bloodless" and "untrodden" has contrasted them with fields that will be trampled with men and horses and their whiteness stained with the blood of both when the sun will be up again.

Poems can belong to us, making us richer—and the fact that

this riches can't be counted up, that it is within us, makes it nonetheless riches. The riches is more secure if we have earned it. We'll go back to the little girl crossing the field with her pailful of water. She earned the richness that lasted through the changes of her life by her labor on those evenings. Her labor was also an act of her heart and mind. We can earn the richness by such an act, perhaps without the labor: the purchase of a book through some saving of ours, the withdrawal from some entertainment to read and reread a poem. Change "learn" into "earn": it is by some act of the heart and mind that we come to know a poem.

Poems are made to be said; they are for our voices, not just for our eyes. It is because he wants us to hear what he made and to speak it that the poet, generally after a difficult search, chooses words that rhyme happily and are enlivening to say. We should say them, sound them. The way to have a poem as a possession is through our ability to say it to ourselves or to others. It is to know it by heart. I am not telling you that all the poems in this collection have to be known by heart. Some favorites, ten or twenty, or more, should be known well enough to say them to ourselves and to others.

And now a word about the kind of poems that are here assembled from the great roll of poetry in English. They have been chosen for certain qualities—visualness, striking imagery, picturesqueness, action, humor. They are poems in which subjectiveness and meditation are not particularly marked. The arrangement is not formal: it is by way of imaginative relationship. Sayers and learners who have been kept in mind are those whose twentieth birthday is still before them.

PADRAIC COLUM

CONTENTS

* The reader is referred to the notes on pages 172–176.

Vision of Belshazzar

LORD BYRON

The King was on his throne,
  The Satraps thronged the hall;
A thousand bright lamps shone
  O'er that high festival.
A thousand cups of gold,
  In Judah deemed divine—
Jehovah's vessels hold
  The godless heathen's wine!

In that same hour and hall,
  The fingers of a hand
Came forth against the wall,
  And wrote as if on sand:
The fingers of a man;—
  A solitary hand
Along the letters ran,
  And traced them like a wand.

The monarch saw, and shook,
  And bade no more rejoice;
All bloodless waxed his look,
  And tremulous his voice.
"Let the men of lore appear,
  The wisest of the earth,
And expound the words of fear,
  Which mar our royal mirth."

Chaldea's seers are good,
  But here they have no skill;
And the unknown letters stood,
  Untold and awful still.

And Babel's men of age
   Are wise and deep in lore;
But now they were not sage,
   They saw—but knew no more.

A captive in the land,
   A stranger and a youth,
He heard the King's command,
   He saw that writing's truth.
The lamps around were bright,
   The prophecy in view;
He read it on that night—
   The morrow proved it true.

"Belshazzar's grave is made,
   His kingdom passed away,
He, in the balance weighed,
   Is light and worthless clay:
The shroud, his robe of state,
   His canopy, the stone:
The Mede is at his gate!
   The Persian on his throne!"

Address to a Mummy

HORACE SMITH

And thou hast walked about (how strange a story!)
In Thebes's streets three thousand years ago,
When the Memnonium was in all its glory,
And time had not begun to overthrow
  Those temples, palaces, and piles stupendous
  Of which the very ruins are tremendous.

* * *

Tell us—for doubtless thou canst recollect,
To whom should we assign the Sphinx's fame?
Was Cheops or Cephrenes architect
Of either pyramid that bears his name?
  Is Pompey's Pillar really a misnomer?
  Had Thebes a hundred gates, as sung by Homer?

* * *

Perchance that very hand, now pinioned flat,
Has hob-a-nobbed with Pharaoh, glass to glass;
Or dropped a halfpenny in Homer's hat,
Or doffed thine own to let Queen Dido pass;
  Or held, by Solomon's own invitation,
  A torch at the great temple's dedication.

I need not ask thee if that hand, when armed,
Has any Roman soldier mauled and knuckled;
For thou wert dead and buried and embalmed
Ere Romulus and Remus had been suckled:
  Antiquity appears to have begun
  Long after thy primeval race was run.

Thou couldst develop, if that withered tongue
Might tell us what those sightless orbs have seen,
How the world looked when it was fresh and young,
And the great deluge still had left it green—
    Or was it then so old that history's pages
    Contained no record of its early ages?

Still silent! incommunicative elf!
Art sworn to secrecy? then keep thy vows;
But prythee tell us something of thyself—
Reveal the secrets of thy prison-house;
    Since in the world of spirits thou hast slumbered,
    What hast thou seen—what strange adventures numbered?

Since first thy form was in this box extended,
We have, above ground, seen some strange mutations.
The Roman empire has begun and ended,
New worlds have risen, we have lost old nations;
    And countless kings have into dust been humbled,
    While not a fragment of thy flesh has crumbled.

Didst thou hear not the pother o'er thy head,
When the great Persian conqueror, Cambyses,
Marched armies o'er thy tomb with thundering tread,
O'erthrew Osiris, Orus, Apis, Isis;
    And shook the pyramids with fear and wonder,
    When the gigantic Memnon fell asunder?

If the tomb's secrets may not be confessed,
The nature of thy private life unfold:
A heart has throbbed beneath that leathern breast,
And tears adown that dusty cheek have rolled:
    Have children climbed those knees, and kissed that face?
    What was thy name and station, age and race?

Statue of flesh—Immortal of the dead!
Imperishable type of evanescence!
Posthumous man, who quit'st thy narrow bed,
And standest undecayed within our presence!
Thou wilt hear nothing till the Judgment morning,
When the great Trump shall thrill thee with its warning.

Why should this worthless tegument endure,
If its undying guest be lost for ever?
O! let us keep the soul embalmed and pure
In living virtue, that when both must sever,
Although corruption may our frame consume,
The immortal spirit in the skies may bloom!

The Time of the Barmacides

JAMES CLARENCE MANGAN

My eyes are filmed, my beard is grey,
I am bowed with the weight of years,
I would I were stretched in my bed of clay
With my long-lost youth's compeers.
For back to the past, though the thought brings woe,
My memory ever glides,
To the old, old time, long, long ago,
To the time of the Barmacides,
To the old, old time long, long ago,
To the time of the Barmacides.

One golden goblet illumined my board,
One silver dish was there,
At hand my tried Karamenian sword
Lay always bright and bare.
For those were the days when the angry blow
Supplanted the word that chides,
And hearts could glow, long, long ago,
In the time of the Barmacides,
And hearts could glow, long, long ago,
In the time of the Barmacides.

I see rich Bagdad once again,
With its turrets of Moorish mould,
And the Khalif's twice five hundred men
Whose binishes flamed with gold.
And I call up many a gorgeous show
That the pall of oblivion hides,
All passed like snow, long, long ago,
In the time of the Barmacides,
All passed like snow, long, long ago,
In the time of the Barmacides.

[8]

But my eyes are dim, my beard is grey,
And I bend with the weight of years,
May I soon go down to my bed of clay
Where slumber my youth's compeers,
For with them in the past, though the thought brings woe,
My memory ever abides,
And I mourn for the time long, long ago,
The time of the Barmacides,
And I mourn for the time gone long ago,
The time of the Barmacides.

The Isles of Greece

LORD BYRON

The isles of Greece! the isles of Greece
  Where burning Sappho loved and sung,
Where grew the arts of war and peace,
  Where Delos rose, and Phoebus sprung!
Eternal summer gilds them yet,
But all, except their sun, is set.

The Scian and the Teian muse,
  The hero's harp, the lover's lute,
Have found the fame your shores refuse:
  Their place of birth alone is mute
To sounds which echo further west
Than your sires' "Islands of the Blest."

The mountains look on Marathon—
  And Marathon looks on the sea;
And musing there an hour alone,
  I dream'd that Greece might still be free;
For standing on the Persians' grave,
I could not deem myself a slave.

A king sate on the rocky brow
  Which looks o'er sea-born Salamis;
And ships, by thousands, lay below,
  And men in nations;—all were his!
He counted them at break of day—
And when the sun set, where were they?

And where are they? and where art thou,
  My country? On thy voiceless shore

The heroic lay is tuneless now—
  The heroic bosom beats no more!
And must thy lyre, so long divine,
Degenerate into hands like mine?

'Tis something in the dearth of fame,
  Though link'd among a fetter'd race,
To feel at least a patriot's shame,
  Even as I sing, suffuse my face;
For what is left the poet here?
For Greeks a blush—for Greece a tear.

Must *we* but weep o'er days more blest?
  Must *we* but blush?—Our fathers bled.
Earth! render back from out thy breast
  A remnant of our Spartan dead!
Of the three hundred grant but three,
To make a new Thermopylae!

What, silent still? and silent all?
  Ah! no;—the voices of the dead
Sound like a distant torrent's fall,
  And answer, "Let one living head,
But one, arise,—we come, we come!"
'Tis but the living who are dumb.

In vain—in vain: strike other chords;
  Fill high the cup with Samian wine!
Leave battles to the Turkish hordes,
  And shed the blood of Scio's vine!
Hark! rising to the ignoble call—
How answers each bold Bacchanal!

You have the Pyrrhic dance as yet;
  Where is the Pyrrhic phalanx gone?

Of two such lessons, why forget
    The nobler and the manlier one?
You have the letters Cadmus gave—
Think ye he meant them for a slave?

Fill high the bowl with Samian wine!
    We will not think of themes like these!
It made Anacreon's song divine:
    He served—but served Polycrates—
A tyrant; but our masters then
Were still, at least, our countrymen.

The tyrant of the Chersonese
    Was freedom's best and bravest friend;
That tyrant was Miltiades!
    O that the present hour would lend
Another despot of the kind!
Such chains as his were sure to bind.

Fill high the bowl with Samian wine!
    On Suli's rock, and Parga's shore,
Exists the remnant of a line
    Such as the Doric mothers bore;
And there, perhaps, some seed is sown,
The Heracleidan blood might own.

Trust not for freedom to the Franks—
    They have a king who buys and sells;
In native swords and native ranks
    The only hope of courage dwells:
But Turkish force and Latin fraud
Would break your shield, however broad.

Fill high the bowl with Samian wine!
    Our virgins dance beneath the shade—

I see their glorious black eyes shine;
    But gazing on each glowing maid,
My own the burning tear-drop laves,
To think such breasts must suckle slaves.

Place me on Sunium's marbled steep,
    Were nothing, save the waves and I,
May hear our mutual murmurs sweep;
    There, swan-like, let me sing and die:
A land of slaves shall ne'er be mine—
Dash down yon cup of Samian wine!

Ozymandias

PERCY BYSSHE SHELLEY

I met a traveller from an antique land
Who said: Two vast and trunkless legs of stone
Stand in the desert. Near them, on the sand,
Half sunk, a shattered visage lies, whose frown,
And wrinkled lip, and sneer of cold command,
Tell that its sculptor well those passions read
Which yet survive, stamped on these lifeless things,
The hand that mocked them and the heart that fed:
And on the pedestal these words appear:
"My name is Ozymandias, king of kings:
Look on my works, ye Mighty, and despair!"
Nothing beside remains. Round the decay
Of that colossal wreck, boundless and bare
The lone and level sands stretch far away.

Kubla Khan

SAMUEL TAYLOR COLERIDGE

In Xanadu did Kubla Khan
A stately pleasure-dome decree:
Where Alph, the sacred river, ran
Through caverns measureless to man
  Down to a sunless sea.
So twice five miles of fertile ground
With walls and towers were girdled round:
And there were gardens bright with sinuous rills,
Where blossomed many an incense-bearing tree;
And here were forests ancient as the hills,
Enfolding sunny spots of greenery.

But oh! that deep romantic chasm which slanted
Down the green hill athwart a cedarn cover!
A savage place! as holy and enchanted
As e'er beneath a waning moon was haunted
By woman wailing for her demon-lover!
And from this chasm, with ceaseless turmoil seething,
As if this earth in fast thick pants were breathing,
A mightly fountain momently was forced:
Amid whose swift half-intermitted burst
Huge fragments vaulted like rebounding hail,
Or chaffy grain beneath the thresher's flail:
And 'mid these dancing rocks at once and ever
It flung up momently the sacred river.
Five miles meandering with a mazy motion
Through wood and dale the sacred river ran,
Then reached the caverns measureless to man,
And sank in tumult to a lifeless ocean:
And 'mid this tumult Kubla heard from far
Ancestral voices prophesying war!

The shadow of the dome of pleasure
　　Floated midway on the waves;
Where was heard the mingled measure
　　From the fountain and the caves.
It was a miracle of rare device,
A sunny pleasure-dome with caves of ice!

A damsel with a dulcimer
　　In a vision once I saw:
It was an Abyssinian maid,
　　And on her dulcimer she played,
　　Singing of Mount Abora.
　　Could I revive within me
　　Her symphony and song,
To such a deep delight 'twould win me,
That with music loud and long,
I would build that dome in air,
That sunny dome! those caves of ice!
And all who heard should see them there,
And all should cry, Beware! Beware!
His flashing eyes, his floating hair!
Weave a circle round him thrice,
　　And close your eyes with holy dread,
　　For he on honey-dew hath fed,
And drunk the milk of Paradise.

On First Looking into Chapman's Homer

JOHN KEATS

Much have I travell'd in the realms of gold,
   And many goodly states and kingdoms seen;
   Round many western islands have I been
Which bards in fealty to Apollo hold.
Oft of one wide expanse had I been told
   That deep-brow'd Homer ruled as his demesne;
   Yet did I never breathe its pure serene
Till I heard Chapman speak out loud and bold:
Then felt I like some watcher of the skies
   When a new planet swims into his ken;
Or like stout Cortez when with eagle eyes
   He stared at the Pacific—and all his men
Look'd at each other with a wild surmise—
   Silent, upon a peak in Darien.

By the Statue of King Charles at Charing Cross

LIONEL JOHNSON

Sombre and rich, the skies,
Great glooms, and starry plains.
Gently the night wind sighs;
Else a vast silence reigns.

The splendid silence clings
Around me: and around
The saddest of all Kings
Crown'd, and again discrown'd.

Comely and calm, he rides
Hard by his own Whitehall.
Only the night wind glides:
No crowds, nor rebels, brawl.

Gone, too, his Court: and yet,
The stars his courtiers are:
Stars in their stations set;
And every wandering star.

Alone he rides, alone,
The fair and fatal King:
Dark night is all his own,
That strange and solemn thing.

Which are more full of fate:
The stars, or those sad eyes?
Which are more still and great:
Those brows, or the dark skies?

Although his whole heart yearn
In passionate tragedy:
Never was face so stern
With sweet austerity.

Vanquish'd in life, his death
By beauty made amends:
The passing of his breath
Won his defeated ends.

Brief life, and hapless? Nay:
Through death, life grew sublime.
Speak after sentence? Yea:
And to the end of time.

Armour'd he rides, his head
Bare to the stars of doom;
He triumphs now, the dead,
Beholding London's gloom.

Our wearier spirit faints,
Vex'd in the world's employ:
His soul was of the saints;
And art to him was joy.

King, tried in fires of woe!
Men hunger for thy grace:
And through the night I go,
Loving thy mournful face.

Yet, when the city sleeps;
When all the cries are still:
The stars and heavenly deeps
Work out a perfect will.

The Harp That Once Through Tara's Halls

THOMAS MOORE

The harp that once through Tara's halls
The soul of music shed,
Now hangs as mute on Tara's walls
As if that soul were fled.
So sleeps the pride of former days,
So glory's thrill is o'er,
And hearts, that once beat high for praise,
Now feel that pulse no more.

No more to chiefs and ladies bright
The harp of Tara swells:
The chord alone, that breaks at night,
Its tale of ruin tells.
Thus Freedom now so seldom wakes,
The only throb she gives
Is when some heart indignant breaks,
To show that still she lives.

When the Assault
Was Intended to the City

JOHN MILTON

Captain or Colonel, or Knight in Arms,
  Whose chance on these defenceless doors may seize,
  If deed of honour did thee ever please,
  Guard them, and him within protect from harms.
He can requite thee; for he knows the charms
  That call fame on such gentle acts as these,
  And he can spread thy name o'er lands and seas,
  Whatever clime the sun's bright circle warms.
Lift not thy spear against the Muses' bower:
  The great Emathian conqueror bid spare
  The house of Pindarus, when temple and tower
Went to the ground; and the repeated air
  Of sad Electra's poet had the power
  To save the Athenian walls from ruin bare.

The Oracles

A. E. HOUSMAN

'Tis mute, the word they went to hear on high Dodona mountain
When winds were in the oakenshaws and all the cauldrons tolled,
And mute's the midland navel-stone beside the singing fountain,
And echoes list to silence now where gods told lies of old.

I took my question to the shrine that has not ceased from
    speaking,
The heart within, that tells the truth and tells it twice as plain;
And from the cave of oracles I heard the priestess shrieking
That she and I should surely die and never live again.

Oh priestess, what you cry is clear, and sound good sense I
    think it;
But let the screaming echoes rest, and froth your mouth no more.
'Tis true there's better boose than brine, but he that drowns
    must drink it;
And oh, my lass, the news is news that men have heard before.

The King with half the East at heel is marched from lands of
    morning;
Their fighters drink the rivers up, their shafts benight the air.
And he that stands will die for nought, and home there's no
    returning.
The Spartans on the sea-wet rock sat down and combed their hair.

The Song of the Western Men

ROBERT STEPHEN HAWKER

A good sword and a trusty hand!
   A merry heart and true!
King James's men shall understand
   What Cornish lads can do.

And have they fix'd the where and when?
   And shall Trelawny die?
Here's twenty thousand Cornish men
   Will know the reason why!

Out spake their captain brave and bold,
   A merry wight was he:
"If London Tower were Michael's hold,
   We'll set Trelawny free!

"We'll cross the Tamar, land to land,
   The Severn is no stay,
With 'one and all,' and hand in hand,
   And who shall bid us nay?

"And when we come to London Wall,
   A pleasant sight to view,
Come forth! come forth, ye cowards all,
   Here's men as good as you!

"Trelawny he's in keep and hold,
   Trelawny he may die;
But here's twenty thousand Cornish bold
   Will know the reason why!"

Hohenlinden

THOMAS CAMPBELL

On Linden, when the sun was low,
All bloodless lay the untrodden snow,
And dark as winter was the flow
   Of Iser, rolling rapidly.

But Linden saw another sight
When the drum beat at dead of night,
Commanding fires of death to light
   The darkness of her scenery.

By torch and trumpet fast arrayed,
Each horseman drew his battle-blade,
And furious every charger neighed
   To join the dreadful revelry.

Then shook the hills with thunder riven,
Then rushed the steed to battle driven,
And louder than the bolts of heaven
   Far flashed the red artillery.

But redder yet that light shall glow
On Linden's hills of stainèd snow
And bloodier yet the torrent flow
   Of Iser, rolling rapidly.

'Tis morn, but scarce yon level sun
Can pierce the war-clouds, rolling dun,
Where furious Frank and fiery Hun
   Shout in their sulphurous canopy.

The combat deepens. On, ye brave,
Who rush to glory, or the grave!
Wave, Munich! all thy banners wave,
  And charge with all thy chivalry!

Few, few shall part where many meet!
The snow shall be their winding-sheet,
And every turf beneath their feet
  Shall be a soldier's sepulchre.

Incident of the French Camp

ROBERT BROWNING

I

You know, we French stormed Ratisbon:
   A mile or so away,
On a little mound, Napoleon
   Stood on our storming-day;
With neck out-thrust, you fancy how,
   Legs wide, arms locked behind,
As if to balance the prone brow
   Oppressive with its mind.

II

Just as perhaps he mused "My plans
   That soar, to earth may fall,
Let once my army-leader Lannes
   Waver at yonder wall,"
Out 'twixt the battery-smokes there flew
   A rider, bound on bound
Full-galloping; nor bridle drew
   Until he reached the mound.

III

Then off there flung in smiling joy,
   And held himself erect
By just his horse's mane, a boy:
   You hardly could suspect—
(So tight he kept his lips compressed,
   Scarce any blood came through)
You looked twice ere you saw his breast
   Was all but shot in two.

IV

"Well," cried he, "Emperor, by God's grace
  We've got you Ratisbon!
The Marshal's in the market-place,
  And you'll be there anon
To see your flag-bird flap his vans
  Where I, to heart's desire,
Perched him!" The chief's eye flashed; his plans
  Soared up again like fire.

V

The chief's eye flashed; but presently
  Softened itself, as sheathes
A film the mother-eagle's eye
  When her bruised eaglet breathes;
"You're wounded!" "Nay," the soldier's pride
  Touched to the quick, he said:
"I'm killed, Sire!" And his chief beside,
  Smiling the boy fell dead.

The Minstrel Boy

THOMAS MOORE

The Minstrel Boy to the war is gone,
   In the ranks of death you'll find him;
His father's sword he hath girded on,
   And his wild harp slung behind him.

"Land of song!" said the warrior-bard,
   "Though all the world betrays thee,
One sword, at least, thy rights shall guard,
   One faithful harp shall praise thee!"

The minstrel fell! but the foeman's chain
   Could not bring his proud soul under;
The harp he loved ne'er spoke again,
   For he tore its chords asunder;

And said: "No chain shall sully thee,
   Thou soul of love and bravery!
Thy songs were made for the brave and free,
   They shall never sound in slavery!"

How They Brought the Good News
from Ghent to Aix

ROBERT BROWNING

I sprang to the stirrup, and Joris, and he;
I galloped, Dirck galloped, we galloped all three;
"Good speed!" cried the watch, as the gatebolts undrew;
"Speed!" echoed the wall to us galloping through;
Behind shut the postern, the lights sank to rest,
And into the midnight we galloped abreast.

Not a word to each other; we kept the great pace
Neck by neck, stride by stride, never changing our place;
I turned in my saddle and made its girths tight,
Then shortened each stirrup, and set the pique right,
Rebuckled the cheek-strap, chained slacker the bit,
Nor galloped less steadily Roland a whit.

'Twas moonset at starting; but while we drew near
Lokeren, the cocks crew and twilight dawned clear;
At Boom, a great yellow star came out to see;
At Düffeld, 'twas morning as plain as could be;
And from Mechelm church-steeple we heard the half-chime,
So Joris broke silence with, "Yet there is time!"

At Aershot, up leaped of a sudden the sun,
And against him the cattle stood black every one,
To stare through the mist at us galloping past,
And I saw my stout galloper Roland at last,
With resolute shoulders, each butting away
The haze, as some bluff river headland its spray:

And his low head and crest, just one sharp ear bent back
For my voice, and the other pricked out on his track;
And one eye's black intelligence,—ever that glance
O'er its white edge at me, his own master, askance!

And the thick heavy spume-flakes which aye and anon
His fierce lips shook upwards in galloping on.

By Hasselt, Dirck groaned; and cried Joris "Stay spur!
Your Roos galloped bravely, the fault's not in her,
We'll remember at Aix"—for one heard the quick wheeze
Of her chest, saw the stretched neck and staggering knees,
And sunk tail, the horrible heave of the flank,
As down on her haunches she shuddered and sank.

So, we were left galloping, Joris and I,
Past Looz and past Tongres, no cloud in the sky;
The broad sun above laughed a pitiless laugh,
'Neath our feet broke the brittle bright stubble like chaff;
Till over by Dalhem a dome-spire sprang white,
And "Gallop," gasped Joris, "for Aix is in sight!"

"How they'll greet us!"—and all in a moment his roan
Rolled neck and croup over, lay dead as a stone;
And there was my Roland to bear the whole weight
Of the news which alone could save Aix from her fate,
With his nostrils like pits full of blood to the brim,
And with circles of red for his eye-sockets' rim.

Then I cast loose my buffcoat, each holster let fall,
Shook off both my jack-boots, let go belt and all,
Stood up in the stirrup, leaned, patted his ear,
Called my Roland his pet-name, my horse without peer;
Clapped my hands, laughed and sang, any noise, bad or good,
Till at length into Aix Roland galloped and stood.

And all I remember is—friends flocking round
As I sat with his head 'twixt my knees on the ground;
And no voice but was praising this Roland of mine,
As I poured down his throat our last measure of wine,
Which (the burgesses voted by common consent)
Was no more than his due who brought good news from Ghent.

Lochinvar

SIR WALTER SCOTT

O, young Lochinvar is come out of the west,
Through all the wide border his steed was the best;
And save his good broadsword, he weapons had none,
He rode all unarmed, and he rode all alone.
So faithful in love, and so dauntless in war,
There never was knight like the young Lochinvar.

He staid not for brake, and he stopped not for stone,
He swam the Eske river where ford there was none;
But, ere he alighted at Netherby gate,
The bride had consented, the gallant came late:
For a laggard in love, and a dastard in war,
Was to wed the fair Ellen of brave Lochinvar.

So boldly he entered the Netherby hall,
Among bride's-men, and kinsmen, and brothers, and all:
Then spoke the bride's father, his hand on his sword,
(For the poor craven bridegroom said never a word,)
"O come ye in peace here, or come ye in war,
Or to dance at our bridal, young Lord Lochinvar?"

"I long woo'd your daughter, my suit you denied;
Love swells like the Solway, but ebbs like its tide;
And now am I come, with this lost love of mine,
To lead but one measure, drink one cup of wine.
There are maidens in Scotland, more lovely by far,
That would gladly be bride to the young Lochinvar."

The bride kissed the goblet; the knight took it up,
He quaffed off the wine, and he threw down the cup.
She looked down to blush, and she looked up to sigh,
With a smile on her lips, and a tear in her eye.
He took her soft hand, ere her mother could bar,
"Now tread we a measure!" said young Lochinvar.

So stately his form, and so lovely her face,
That never a hall such a galliard did grace:
While her mother did fret, and her father did fume,
And the bridegroom stood dangling his bonnet and plume;
And the bride-maidens whispered, " 'Twere better by far
To have matched our fair cousin with young Lochinvar."

One touch to her hand, and one word in her ear,
When they reached the hall-door, and the charger stood near;
So light to the croupe the fair lady he swung,
So light to the saddle before her he sprung!
"She is won! we are gone, over bank, bush, and scaur;
They'll have fleet steeds that follow," quoth young Lochinvar.

There was mounting 'mong Græmes of the Netherby clan;
Forsters, Fenwicks, and Musgraves, they rode and they ran:
There was racing and chasing, on Cannobie Lee,
But the lost bride of Netherby ne'er did they see.
So daring in love, and so dauntless in war,
Have ye e'er heard of gallant like young Lochinvar?

The Burial of Sir John Moore

CHARLES WOLFE

Not a drum was heard, not a funeral note,
   As his corse to the rampart we hurried;
Not a soldier discharged his farewell shot
   O'er the grave where our hero we buried.

We buried him darkly, at dead of night,
   The sods with our bayonets turning,
By the struggling moonbeam's misty light,
   And the lantern dimly burning.

No useless coffin enclosed his breast,
   Not in sheet nor in shroud we wound him;
But he lay like a warrior taking his rest,
   With his martial cloak around him.

Few and short were the prayers we said,
   And we spake not a word of sorrow;
But we steadfastly gazed on the face that was dead,
   And we bitterly thought of the morrow.

We thought, as we hollowed his narrow bed
   And smoothed down his lonely pillow,
That the foe and the stranger would tread o'er his head,
   And we far away on the billow!

Lightly they'll talk of the spirit that's gone,
   And o'er his cold ashes upbraid him,—
But little he'll reck, if they let him sleep on
   In the grave where a Briton has laid him.

But half of our heavy task was done,
  When the clock struck the hour for retiring,
And we heard the distant and random gun
  That the foe was sullenly firing.

Slowly and sadly we laid him down,
  From the field of his fame fresh and gory;
We carved not a line, and we raised not a stone—
  But we left him alone in his glory!

Relieving Guard

BRET HARTE

Came the Relief. "What, Sentry, Ho!
How passed the night through thy long waking?"
"Cold, cheerless, dark,—as may befit
The hour before the dawn is breaking."

"No sight? no sound?" "No; nothing save
The plover from the marshes calling,
And in yon Western sky, about
An hour ago, a star was falling."

"A star? There's nothing strange in that."
"No, nothing; but, above the thicket,
Somehow it seemed to me that God
Somewhere had just relieved a picket."

O Captain! My Captain!

WALT WHITMAN

O Captain! my Captain! our fearful trip is done,
The ship has weathered every rack, the prize we sought is won,
The port is near, the bells I hear, the people all exulting,
While follow eyes the steady keel, the vessel grim and daring;
But O heart! heart! heart!
O the bleeding drops of red,
Where on the deck my Captain lies,
Fallen cold and dead.

O Captain! my Captain! rise up and hear the bells;
Rise up—for you the flag is flung—for you the bugle trills,
For you bouquets and ribboned wreaths—for you the shores
a-crowding,
For you they call, the swaying mass, their eager faces turning,
Here Captain! dear father!
This arm beneath your head!
It is some dream that on the deck,
You've fallen cold and dead.

My Captain does not answer, his lips are pale and still,
My father does not feel my arm, he has no pulse nor will,
The ship is anchored safe and sound, its voyage closed and done,
From fearful trip the victor ship comes in with object won;
Exult O shores, and ring O bells!
But I with mournful tread,
Walk the deck my Captain lies,
Fallen cold and dead.

Night Encampment Outside Troy

(FROM THE ILIAD)

LORD TENNYSON

So Hector spake; the Trojans roar'd applause;
Then loosed their sweating horses from the yoke,
And each beside his chariot bound his own;
And oxen from the city, and goodly sheep
In haste they drove, and honey-hearted wine
And bread from out the houses brought, and heap'd
Their firewood, and the winds from off the plain
Roll'd the rich vapor far into the heaven.
And these all night upon the bridge of war
Sat glorying; many a fire before them blazed.
As when in heaven the stars about the moon
Look beautiful, when all the winds are laid,
And every height comes out, and jutting peak
And valley, and the immeasurable heavens
Break open to their highest, and all the stars
Shine, and the shepherd gladdens in his heart;
So many a fire between the ships and stream
Of Xanthus blazed before the towers of Troy,
A thousand on the plain; and close by each
Sat fifty in the blaze of the burning fire;
And eating hoary grain and pulse the steeds,
Fixt by their cars, waited the golden dawn.

The Soldier's Dream

THOMAS CAMPBELL

Our bugles sang truce, for the night-cloud had lowered,
   And the sentinel stars set their watch in the sky;
And thousands had sunk on the ground overpowered,
   The weary to sleep, and the wounded to die.

When reposing that night on my pallet of straw,
   By the wolf-scaring faggot that guarded the slain,
At the dead of the night a sweet vision I saw;
   And thrice ere the morning I dreamt it again.

Methought from the battle-field's dreadful array
   Far, far I had roamed on a desolate track:
'Twas Autumn, and sunshine arose on the way
   To the home of my fathers, that welcomed me back.

I flew to the pleasant fields traversed so oft
   In life's morning march, when my bosom was young;
I heard my own mountain-goats bleating aloft,
   And knew the sweet strain that the corn-reapers sung.

Then pledged we the wine-cup, and fondly I swore
   From my home and my weeping friends never to part;
My little ones kissed me a thousand times o'er,
   And my wife sobbed aloud in her fulness of heart.

"Stay—stay with us!—rest!—thou art weary and worn!"
   And fain was their war-broken soldier to stay;
But sorrow returned with the dawning of morn,
   And the voice in my dreaming ear melted away.

Storm at Sea

SIR WILLIAM DAVENANT

Blow! blow! The winds are so hoarse they cannot blow!
Cold! cold! Our tears freeze to hail, our spittle to snow!
The waves are all up, they swell as they run!
       Let them rise and rise,
       As high as the skies,
And higher to wash the face of the sun.

Port! Port! the pilot is blind. Port at the helm!
Yare! yare! for one foot of shore take a whole realm!
A-lee, or we sink! does no man know how to wind her?
       Less noise and more room!
       We sail in a drum!
Our sails are but rags, which lightning turns to tinder.

Aloof! aloof! Hey how those carracks and ships
Fall foul and are tumbled and driven like chips!
Our boatswain, alas! a silly weak gristle,
       For fear to catch cold,
       Lies down in the hold,
We all hear his sighs but few hear his whistle.

On the Loss of the Royal George

WILLIAM COWPER

Toll for the brave!
The brave that are no more!
    All sunk beneath the wave,
Fast by their native shore!

Eight hundred of the brave,
Whose courage well was tried,
    Had made the vessel heel
And laid her on her side.

A land-breeze shook the shrouds,
And she was overset;
    Down went the *Royal George*,
With all her crew complete.

Toll for the brave!
Brave Kempenfelt is gone;
    His last sea-fight is fought;
His work of glory done.

It was not in the battle;
No tempest gave the shock;
    She sprang no fatal leak;
She ran upon no rock.

His sword was in the sheath;
His fingers held the pen,
    When Kempenfelt went down
With twice four hundred men.

Weigh the vessel up,
Once dreaded by our foes!
  And mingle with our cup
The tears that England owes.

  Her timbers yet are sound,
And she may float again
  Full charg'd with England's thunder,
And plough the distant main.

  But Kempenfelt is gone,
His victories are o'er;
  And he and his eight hundred
Shall plough the wave no more.

The Battle of the Baltic

THOMAS CAMPBELL

Of Nelson and the North,
Sing the glorious day's renown,
When to battle fierce came forth
All the might of Denmark's crown,
And her arms along the deep proudly shone;
By each gun the lighted brand
In a bold determined hand,
And the Prince of all the land
Led them on.

Like leviathans afloat,
Lay their bulwarks on the brine;
While the sign of battle flew
On the lofty British line:
It was ten of April morn by the chime:
As they drifted on their path
There was silence deep as death,
And the boldest held his breath,
For a time.

But the might of England flush'd
To anticipate the scene;
And her van the fleeter rush'd
O'er the deadly space between:
"Hearts of oak!" our captains cried, when each gun
From its adamantine lips
Spread a death-shade round the ships,
Like the hurricane eclipse
Of the sun.

Again! again! again!
And the havoc did not slack,
Till a feeble cheer the Dane
To our cheering sent us back;—
Their shots along the deep slowly boom:—
Then ceased—and all is wail,
As they strike the shatter'd sail;
Or in conflagration pale,
Light the gloom.

Out spoke the victor then
As he hailed them o'er the wave:
"Ye are brothers! ye are men!
And we conquer but to save:—
So peace instead of death let us bring:
But yield, proud foe, thy fleet,
With the crews, at England's feet,
And make submission meet
To our King."

Then Denmark blessed our chief,
That he gave her wounds repose;
And the sounds of joy and grief,
From her people wildly rose,
As death withdrew his shades from the day;
While the sun looked smiling bright
O'er a wide and woeful sight,
Where the fires of funeral light
Died away.

Now joy, old England, raise!
For the tidings of thy might,
By the festal cities' blaze,

Whilst the wine-cup shines in light!
And yet, amidst that joy and uproar,
Let us think of them that sleep
Full many a fathom deep,
By thy wild and stormy steep,
Elsinore!

Brave hearts! to Britain's pride
Once so faithful and so true,
On the deck of fame that died;
With the gallant good Riou:
Soft sigh the winds of Heaven o'er their grave!
While the billow mournful rolls,
And the mermaid's song condoles,
Singing glory to the souls
Of the brave!

A Wet Sheet and a Flowing Sea

ALLAN CUNNINGHAM

A wet sheet and a flowing sea,
  A wind that follows fast,
And fills the white and rustling sail
  And bends the gallant mast;
And bends the gallant mast, my boys,
  While, like the eagle free,
Away the good ship flies, and leaves
  Old England on the lee.

"O for a soft and gentle wind!"
  I heard a fair one cry;
But give to me the snoring breeze
  And white waves heaving high;
And white waves heaving high, my lads,
  The good ship tight and free—
The world of waters is our home,
  And merry men are we.

There's tempest in yon hornèd moon,
  And lightning in yon cloud;
But hark the music, mariners!
  The wind is piping loud;
The wind is piping loud, my boys,
  The lightning flashes free—
While the hollow oak our palace is,
  Our heritage the sea.

Lord Ullin's Daughter

THOMAS CAMPBELL

A Chieftain, to the Highlands bound,
Cries, "Boatman, do not tarry!
And I'll give thee a silver pound
To row us o'er the ferry."

"Now who be ye, would cross Lochgyle,
This dark and stormy water?"
"Oh, I'm the Chief of Ulva's isle,
And this, Lord Ullin's daughter.

"And fast before her father's men
Three days we've fled together,
For should he find us in the glen
My blood would stain the heather.

"His horsemen hard behind us ride;
Should they our steps discover,
Then who will cheer my bonny bride
When they have slain her lover?"

Out spoke the hardy Highland wight,
"I'll go, my Chief—I'm ready:
It is not for your silver bright
But for your winsome lady:

"And by my word! the bonny bird
In danger shall not tarry;
So though the waves are raging white,
I'll row you o'er the ferry."

By this the storm grew loud apace,
The water-wraith was shrieking;

And in the scowl of heaven each face
Grew dark as they were speaking.

But still as wilder blew the wind,
And as the night grew drearer,
Adown the glen rode armed men,
Their trampling sounded nearer.

"Oh haste thee, haste!" the lady cries,
"Though tempests round us gather;
I'll meet the raging of the skies
But not an angry father."

The boat has left a stormy land,
A stormy sea before her,
When, Oh! too strong for human hand
The tempest gathered o'er her.

But still they rowed amidst the roar
Of waters fast prevailing:
Lord Ullin reached that fatal shore,
His wrath was changed to wailing.

For, sore dismayed, through storm and shade
His child he did discover:
One lovely hand she stretched for aid,
And one was round her lover.

"Come back! come back!" he cried in grief
Across this stormy water:
"And I'll forgive your Highland chief,
My daughter! Oh, my daughter!"

'Twas vain: the loud waves lashed the shore,
Return or aid preventing:
The waters wild went o'er his child,
And he was left lamenting.

Tristan da Cunha

ROY CAMPBELL

Snore in the foam; the night is vast and blind;
The blanket of the mist around your shoulders,
Sleep your old sleep of rock, snore in the wind,
Snore in the spray! The storm your slumber lulls,
His wings are folded on your nest of boulders
As on their eggs the grey wings of your gulls.

No more as when, so dark an age ago,
You hissed a giant cinder from the ocean,
Around your rocks you furl the shawling snow
Half sunk in your own darkness, vast and grim,
And round you on the deep with surly motion
Pivot your league-long shadow as you swim.

Why should you haunt me thus but that I know
My surly heart is in your own displayed,
Round whom such leagues in endless circuit flow,
Whose hours in such a gloomy compass run—
A dial with its league-long arm of shade
Slowly revolving to the moon and sun.

My pride has sunk, like your grey fissured crags,
By its own strength o'ertoppled and betrayed:
I, too, have burned the wind with fiery flags
Who now am but a roost for empty words,
An island of the sea whose only trade
Is in the voyage of its wandering birds.

Did you not, when your strength became your pyre
Deposed and tumbled from your flaming tower,
Awake in gloom from whence you sank in fire,

To find, Antaeus-like, more vastly grown,
A throne in your own darkness, and a power
Sheathed in the very coldness of your stone?

Your strength is that you have no hope or fear,
You march before the world without a crown,
The nations call you back, you do not hear,
The cities of the earth grow grey behind you,
You will be there when their great flames go down
And still the morning in the van will find you.

You march before the continents, you scout
In front of all the earth; alone you scale
The mast-head of the world, a lorn look-out,
Waving the snowy flutter of your spray
And gazing back in infinite farewell
To suns that sink and shores that fade away.

From your grey tower what long regrets you fling
To where, along the low horizon burning,
The great swan-breasted seraphs soar and sing,
And suns go down, and trailing splendours dwindle,
And sails on lonely errands unreturning
Glow with a gold no sunrise can rekindle.

Turn to the night these flames are not for you,
Whose steeple for the thunder swings its bells;
Grey Memnon, to the tempest only true,
Turn to the night, turn to the shadowing foam,
And let your voice, the saddest of farewells,
With sullen curfew toll the grey wings home.

The wind, your mournful syren, haunts the gloom;
The rocks, spray-clouded, are your signal guns
Whose stony nitre, puffed with flying spume,

Rolls forth in grim salute your broadside hollow
Over the gorgeous burials of suns
To sound the tocsin of the storms that follow.

Plunge forward like a ship to battle hurled,
Slip the long cables of the failing light,
The level rays that moor you to the world:
Sheathed in your armour of eternal frost,
Plunge forward, in the thunder of the fight
To lose yourself as I would fain be lost.

Exiled like you and severed from my race
By the cold ocean of my own disdain,
Do I not freeze in such a wintry space,
Do I not travel through a storm as vast
And rise at times, victorious from the main,
To fly the sunrise at my shattered mast?

Your path is but a desert where you reap
Only the bitter knowledge of your soul:
You fish with nets of seaweed in the deep
As fruitlessly as I with nets of rhyme—
Yet forth you stride, yourself the way, the goal,
The surges are your strides, your path is time.

Hurled by what aim to what tremendous range!
A missile from the great sling of the past,
Your passage leaves its track of death and change
And ruin on the world: you fly beyond
Leaping the current of the ages vast
As lightly as a pebble skims a pond.

The years are undulations in your flight
Whose awful motion we can only guess—
Too swift for sense, too terrible for sight,

We only know how fast behind you darken
Our days like lonely beacons of distress:
We know that you stride on and will not harken.

Now in the eastern sky the fairest planet
Pierces the dying wave with dangled spear,
And in the whirring hollows of your granite
That vaster sea to which you are a shell
Sighs with a ghostly rumour, like the drear
Moan of the nightwind in a hollow cell.

We shall not meet again; over the wave
Our ways divide, and yours is straight and endless,
But mine is short and crooked to the grave:
Yet what of these dark crowds amid whose flow
I battle like a rock, aloof and friendless,
Are not their generations vague and endless
The waves, the strides, the feet on which I go?

Cargoes

JOHN MASEFIELD

Quinquireme of Nineveh from distant Ophir
Rowing home to haven in sunny Palestine,
With a cargo of ivory,
And apes and peacocks,
Sandalwood, cedarwood, and sweet white wine.

Stately Spanish galleon coming from the Isthmus,
Dipping through the Tropics by the palm-green shores,
With a cargo of diamonds,
Emeralds, amethysts,
Topazes, and cinnamon, and gold moidores.

Dirty British coaster with a salt-caked smoke-stack
Butting through the Channel in the mad March days,
With a cargo of Tyne coal,
Road-rail, pig-lead,
Firewood, iron-ware, and cheap tin trays.

The Old Ships

JAMES ELROY FLECKER

I have seen old ships sail like swans asleep
Beyond the village which men still call Tyre,
With leaden age o'ercargoed, dipping deep
For Famagusta and the hidden sun
That rings black Cyprus with a lake of fire;
And all those ships were certainly so old—
Who knows how oft with squat and noisy gun,
Questing brown slaves or Syrian oranges,
The pirate Genoese
Hell-raked them till they rolled
Blood, water, fruit and corpses up the hold?
But now through friendly seas they softly run,
Painted the mid-sea blue or shore-sea green,
Still patterned with the vine and grapes in gold.

But I have seen,
Pointing her shapely shadows from the dawn
An image tumbled on a rose-swept bay;
A drowsy ship of some yet older day;
And, wonder's breath indrawn,
Thought I—who knows—who knows but in that same
(Fished up beyond Aeaea, patched up new
—Stern painted brighter blue—)
That talkative bald-headed seaman came
(Twelve patient comrades sweating at the oar)
From Troy's doom-crimson shore,
And with great lies about his wooden horse
Set the crew laughing, and forgot his course?
It was so old a ship—who knows, who knows?
—And yet so beautiful, I watched in vain
To see the mast burst open with a rose,
And the whole deck put on its leaves again.

The Ballad of
Sir Patrick Spens

ANONYMOUS

The King sits in Dunferling toune,
Drinking the blude-red wine:
"O wher will I get a guid sailor,
To sail this schip of mine?"

Up and spak an eldern knicht,
Sat at the king's richt knee,
"Sir Patrick Spens is the best sailor
That sails upon the sea."

The King has written a braid letter,
And signed it with his hand,
And sent it to Sir Patrick Spens,
Was walking on the sand.

The first line that Sir Patrick read,
A loud lauch lauched he;
The next line that Sir Patrick read,
The tear blinded his ee.

"O wha is this has done this deid,
This ill deid done to me,
To send me out this time o' the year
To sail upon the sea?

Mak haste, mak haste, my merry men all,
Our guid schip sails this morn."
"O say na so, my master deir,
For I fear a deadlie storm.

"Late, late yestreen I saw the new moon
Wi' the auld moon in her arm,
And I fear, I fear, my deir master,
That we will come to harm."

O our Scots nobles were richt laith
To wet their cork-heeled schoon;
But lang owre a' the play was played,
Their hats they swam aboon.

O lang, lang may their ladies sit,
Wi' their fans into their hand,
Or e'er they see Sir Patrick Spens
Come sailing to the land.

O lang, lang, may the ladies stand,
Wi' their gold combs in their hair,
Waiting for their own dear lords,
For they 'll see them na mair.

Half owre, half owre to Aberdour,
It's fifty fathom deep,
And there lies guid Sir Patrick Spens,
Wi' the Scots lords at his feet.

Lauch: laugh
Laith: loth, unwilling
Owre: before
Swam aboon: floated above

The Rime of the Ancient Mariner

SAMUEL TAYLOR COLERIDGE

PART I

It is an ancient Mariner,
And he stoppeth one of three.
"By thy long grey beard and glittering eye,
Now wherefore stopp'st thou me?

The Bridegroom's doors are open'd wide,
And I am next of kin;
The guests are met, the feast is set:
May'st hear the merry din."

He holds him with his skinny hand,
"There was a ship," quoth he.
"Hold off! unhand me, grey-beard loon!"
Eftsoons his hand dropt he.

He holds him with his glittering eye—
The Wedding-Guest stood still,
And listens like a three years' child:
The Mariner hath his will.

The Wedding-Guest sat on a stone:
He cannot choose but hear;
And thus spake on that ancient man,
The bright-eyed Mariner.

"The ship was cheer'd, the harbour clear'd,
Merrily did we drop
Below the kirk, below the hill,
Below the lighthouse top.

The Sun came up upon the left,
Out of the sea came he!
And he shone bright, and on the right
Went down into the sea.

Higher and higher every day,
Till over the mast at noon—"
The Wedding-Guest here beat his breast,
For he heard the loud bassoon.

The bride hath paced into the hall,
Red as a rose is she;
Nodding their heads before her goes
The merry minstrelsy.

The Wedding-Guest he beat his breast,
Yet he cannot choose but hear;
And thus spake on that ancient man,
The bright-eyed Mariner.

"And now the Storm-blast came, and he
Was tyrannous and strong:
He struck with his o'ertaking wings,
And chased us south along.

With sloping masts and dipping prow,
As who pursued with yell and blow
Still treads the shadow of his foe,
And forward bends his head,
The ship drove fast, loud roar'd the blast,
And southward aye we fled.

And now there came both mist and snow,
And it grew wondrous cold:
And ice, mast-high, came floating by,
As green as emerald.

And through the drifts the snowy clifts
Did send a dismal sheen:
Nor shapes of men nor beasts we ken—
The ice was all between.

The ice was here, the ice was there,
The ice was all around:
It crack'd and growl'd, and roar'd and howl'd,
Like noises in a swound!

At length did cross an Albatross,
Through the fog it came;
As if it had been a Christian soul,
We hail'd it in God's name.

It ate the food it ne'er had eat,
And round and round it flew.
The ice did split with a thunder-fit;
The helmsman steer'd us through!

And a good south wind sprung up behind;
The Albatross did follow,
And every day, for food or play,
Came to the mariners' hollo!

In mist or cloud, on mast or shroud,
It perch'd for vespers nine;
While all the night, through fog-smoke white,
Glimmer'd the white moonshine."

"God save thee, ancient Mariner,
From the fiends that plague thee thus!
Why look'st thou so?"—"With my crossbow
I shot the Albatross.

PART II

"The Sun now rose upon the right:
Out of the sea came he,
Still hid in mist, and on the left
Went down into the sea.

And the good south wind still blew behind,
But no sweet bird did follow,
Nor any day for food or play
Came to the mariners' hollo!

And I had done an hellish thing,
And it would work 'em woe:
For all averr'd I had kill'd the bird
That made the breeze to blow.
Ah wretch! said they, the bird to slay,
That made the breeze to blow!

Nor dim nor red, like God's own head,
The glorious Sun uprist:
Then all averr'd I had kill'd the bird
That brought the fog and mist.
'Twas right, said they, such birds to slay,
That bring the fog and mist.

The fair breeze blew, the white foam flew,
The furrow follow'd free;
We were the first that ever burst
Into that silent sea.

Down dropt the breeze, the sails dropt down,
'Twas sad as sad could be;
And we did speak only to break
The silence of the sea!

All in a hot and copper sky,
The bloody Sun, at noon,
Right up above the mast did stand,
No bigger than the Moon.

Day after day, day after day,
We stuck, nor breath nor motion;
As idle as a painted ship
Upon a painted ocean.

Water, water, everywhere,
And all the boards did shrink;
Water, water, everywhere,
Nor any drop to drink.

The very deep did rot: O Christ!
That ever this should be!
Yea, slimy things did crawl with legs
Upon the slimy sea.

About, about, in reel and rout
The death-fires danced at night;
The water, like a witch's oils,
Burnt green, and blue, and white.

And some in dreams assurèd were
Of the Spirit that plagued us so;
Nine fathom deep he had follow'd us
From the land of mist and snow.

And every tongue, through utter drought,
Was wither'd at the root;
We could not speak, no more than if
We had been choked with soot.

Ah! well a-day! what evil looks
Had I from old and young!
Instead of the cross, the Albatross
About my neck was hung.

PART III

"There passed a weary time. Each throat
Was parch'd, and glazed each eye.
A weary time! a weary time!
How glazed each weary eye!
When, looking westward, I beheld
A something in the sky.

At first it seem'd a little speck,
And then it seem'd a mist;
It moved and moved, and took at last
A certain shape, I wist.

A speck, a mist, a shape, I wist!
And still it near'd and near'd:
As if it dodged a water-sprite,
It plunged, and tack'd and veer'd.

With throats unslaked, with black lips baked,
We could nor laugh nor wail;
Through utter drought all dumb we stood!
I bit my arm, I suck'd the blood,
And cried, A sail! a sail!

With throats unslaked, with black lips baked,
Agape they heard me call:
Gramercy! they for joy did grin,
And all at once their breath drew in,
As they were drinking all.

See! see! (I cried) she tacks no more!
Hither to work us weal—
Without a breeze, without a tide,
She steadies with upright keel!

The western wave was all aflame,
The day was wellnigh done!
Almost upon the western wave
Rested the broad, bright Sun;
When that strange shape drove suddenly
Betwixt us and the Sun.

And straight the Sun was fleck'd with bars
(Heaven's Mother send us grace!)
As if through a dungeon-grate he peer'd
With broad and burning face.

Alas! (thought I, and my heart beat loud)
How fast she nears and nears!
Are those her sails that glance in the Sun,
Like restless gossameres?

Are those her ribs through which the Sun
Did peer, as through a grate?
And is that Woman all her crew
Is that a Death? and are there two?
Is Death that Woman's mate?

Her lips were red, her looks were free,
Her locks were yellow as gold:
Her skin was as white as leprosy,
The Nightmare Life-in-Death was she,
Who thicks man's blood with cold.

The naked hulk alongside came,
And the twain were casting dice;

'The game is done! I've won! I've won!'
Quoth she, and whistles thrice.

The Sun's rim dips; the stars rush out:
At one stride comes the dark;
With far-heard whisper, o'er the sea,
Off shot the spectre-bark.

We listen'd and look'd sideways up!
Fear at my heart, as at a cup,
My life-blood seem'd to sip!
The stars were dim, and thick the night,
The steersman's face by his lamp gleam'd white;
From the sails the dew did drip—
Till clomb above the eastern bar
The hornèd Moon, with one bright star
Within the nether tip.

One after one, by the star-dogg'd Moon,
Too quick for groan or sigh,
Each turn'd his face with a ghastly pang,
And cursed me with his eye.

Four times fifty living men
(And I heard nor sigh nor groan),
With heavy thump, a lifeless lump,
They dropp'd down one by one.

The souls did from their bodies fly—
They fled to bliss or woe!
And every soul, it pass'd me by
Like the whizz of my crossbow!"

PART IV

"I fear thee, ancient Mariner!
I fear thy skinny hand!

And thou art long, and lank, and brown,
As is the ribb'd sea-sand.

I fear thee and thy glittering eye,
And thy skinny hand so brown."
"Fear not, fear not, thou Wedding-Guest!
This body dropt not down.

Alone, alone, all, all alone,
Alone on a wide, wide sea!
And never a saint took pity on
My soul in agony.

The many men, so beautiful!
And they all dead did lie;
And a thousand thousand slimy things
Lived on; and so did I.

I look'd upon the rotting sea,
And drew my eyes away;
I look'd upon the rotting deck,
And there the dead men lay.

I look'd to heaven, and tried to pray;
But or ever a prayer had gusht,
A wicked whisper came, and made
My heart as dry as dust.

I closed my lids, and kept them close,
And the balls like pulses beat;
But the sky and the sea, and the sea and the sky,
Lay like a load on my weary eye,
And the dead were at my feet.

The cold sweat melted from their limbs,
Nor rot nor reek did they:

The look with which they look'd on me
Had never pass'd away.

An orphan's curse would drag to hell
A spirit from on high;
But oh! more horrible than that
Is the curse in a dead man's eye!
Seven days, seven nights, I saw that curse,
And yet I could not die.

The moving Moon went up the sky,
And nowhere did abide;
Softly she was going up,
And a star or two beside—

Her beams bemock'd the sultry main,
Like April hoar-frost spread;
But where the ship's huge shadow lay,
The charmèd water burnt alway
A still and awful red.

Beyond the shadow of the ship,
I watch'd the water-snakes:
They moved in tracks of shining white
And when they rear'd, the elfish light
Fell off in hoary flakes.

Within the shadow of the ship
I watch'd their rich attire:
Blue, glossy green, and velvet black,
They coil'd and swam; and every track
Was a flash of golden fire.

O happy living things! No tongue
Their beauty might declare:
A spring of love gush'd from my heart,

And I bless'd them unaware:
Sure my kind saint took pity on me,
And I bless'd them unaware.

The selfsame moment I could pray;
And from my neck so free
The Albatross fell off, and sank
Like lead into the sea.

PART V

"O sleep! it is a gentle thing,
Beloved from pole to pole!
To Mary Queen the praise be given!
She sent the gentle sleep from Heaven,
That slid into my soul.

The silly buckets on the deck,
That had so long remain'd,
I dreamt that they were fill'd with dew;
And when I awoke, it rain'd.

My lips were wet, my throat was cold,
My garments all were dank;
Sure I had drunken in my dreams,
And still my body drank.

I moved, and could not feel my limbs:
I was so light—almost
I thought that I had died in sleep,
And was a blessèd ghost.

And soon I heard a roaring wind:
It did not come anear;
But with its sound it shook the sails,
That were so thin and sere.

The upper air burst into life;
And a hundred fire-flags sheen;
To and fro they were hurried about!
And to and fro, and in and out,
The wan stars danced between.

And the coming wind did roar more loud,
And the sails did sigh like sedge;
And the rain pour'd down from one black cloud;
The Moon was at its edge.

The thick black cloud was cleft, and still
The Moon was at its side;
Like waters shot from some high crag,
The lightning fell with never a jag,
A river steep and wide.

The loud wind never reach'd the ship,
Yet now the ship moved on!
Beneath the lightning and the Moon
The dead men gave a groan.

They groan'd, they stirr'd, they all uprose,
Nor spake, nor moved their eyes;
It had been strange, even in a dream,
To have seen those dead men rise.

The helmsman steer'd, the ship moved on;
Yet never a breeze up-blew;
The mariners all 'gan work the ropes,
Where they were wont to do;
They raised their limbs like lifeless tools—
We were a ghastly crew.

The body of my brother's son
Stood by me, knee to knee:

The body and I pull'd at one rope,
But he said naught to me."

"I fear thee, ancient Mariner!"
"Be calm, thou Wedding-Guest:
'Twas not those souls that fled in pain,
Which to their corses came again,
But a troop of spirits blest:

For when it dawn'd—they dropp'd their arms,
And cluster'd round the mast;
Sweet sounds rose slowly through their mouths,
And from their bodies pass'd.

Around, around, flew each sweet sound,
Then darted to the Sun;
Slowly the sounds came back again,
Now mix'd, now one by one.

Sometimes a-dropping from the sky
I heard the skylark sing;
Sometimes all little birds that are,
How they seem'd to fill the sea and air
With their sweet jargoning!

And now 'twas like all instruments,
Now like a lonely flute;
And now it is an angel's song,
That makes the Heavens be mute.

It ceased; yet still the sails made on
A pleasant noise till noon,
A noise like of a hidden brook
In the leafy month of June,
That to the sleeping woods all night
Singeth a quiet tune.

Till noon we quietly sail'd on,
Yet never a breeze did breathe:
Slowly and smoothly went the ship,
Moved onward from beneath.

Under the keel nine fathom deep,
From the land of mist and snow,
The Spirit slid: and it was he
That made the ship to go.
The sails at noon left off their tune,
And the ship stood still also.

The Sun, right up above the mast,
Had fix'd her to the ocean:
But in a minute she 'gan stir,
With a short uneasy motion—
Backwards and forwards half her length
With a short uneasy motion.

Then like a pawing horse let go,
She made a sudden bound:
It flung the blood into my head,
And I fell down in a swound.

How long in that same fit I lay,
I have not to declare;
But ere my living life return'd,
I heard, and in my soul discern'd
Two voices in the air.

'Is it he?' quoth one, 'is this the man?
By Him who died on cross,
With his cruel bow he laid full low
The harmless Albatross.

The Spirit who bideth by himself
In the land of mist and snow,
He loved the bird that loved the man
Who shot him with his bow.'

The other was a softer voice,
As soft as honey-dew:
Quoth he, 'The man hath penance done,
And penance more will do.'

PART VI

First Voice:
" 'But tell me, tell me! speak again,
Thy soft response renewing—
What makes that ship drive on so fast?
What is the Ocean doing?'

Second Voice:
'Still as a slave before his lord,
The Ocean hath no blast;
His great bright eye most silently
Up to the Moon is cast—

If he may know which way to go;
For she guides him smooth or grim.
See, brother, see! how graciously
She looketh down on him.'

First Voice:
'But why drives on that ship so fast,
Without or wave or wind?'

Second Voice:
'The air is cut away before,
And closes from behind.

Fly, brother, fly! more high, more high!
Or we shall be belated:
For slow and slow that ship will go,
When the Mariner's trance is abated.'

I woke, and we were sailing on
As in a gentle weather:
'Twas night, calm night, the Moon was high;
The dead men stood together.

All stood together on the deck,
For a charnel-dungeon fitter:
All fix'd on me their stony eyes,
That in the Moon did glitter.

The pang, the curse, with which they died,
Had never pass'd away:
I could not draw my eyes from theirs,
Nor turn them up to pray.

And now this spell was snapt: once more
I viewed the ocean green,
And look'd far forth, yet little saw
Of what had else been seen—

Like one that on a lonesome road
Doth walk in fear and dread,
And having once turn'd round, walks on,
And turns no more his head;
Because he knows a frightful fiend
Doth close behind him tread.

But soon there breathed a wind on me,
Nor sound nor motion made:
Its path was not upon the sea,
In ripple or in shade.

It raised my hair, it fann'd my cheek
Like a meadow-gale of spring—
It mingled with my fears,
Yet it felt like a welcoming.

Swiftly, swiftly flew the ship,
Yet she sail'd softly too:
Sweetly, sweetly blew the breeze—
On me alone it blew.

O dream of joy! is this indeed
The lighthouse top I see?
Is this the hill? is this the kirk?
Is this mine own countree?

We drifted o'er the harbour-bar,
And I with sobs did pray—
O let me be awake, my God!
Or let me sleep alway.

The harbour-bay was clear as glass,
So smoothly it was strewn!
And on the bay the moonlight lay,
And the shadow of the Moon.

The rock shone bright, the kirk no less
That stands above the rock:
The moonlight steep'd in silentness
The steady weathercock.

And the bay was white with silent light
Till rising from the same,
Full many shapes, that shadows were,
In crimson colours came.

A little distance from the prow
Those crimson shadows were:
I turn'd my eyes upon the deck—
O Christ! what saw I there!

Each corse lay flat, lifeless and flat,
And, by the holy rood!
A man all light, a seraph-man,
On every corse there stood.

This seraph-band, each waved his hand:
It was a heavenly sight!
They stood as signals to the land,
Each one a lovely light;

This seraph-band, each waved his hand,
No voice did they impart—
No voice; but O, the silence sank
Like music on my heart.

But soon I heard the dash of oars,
I heard the Pilot's cheer;
My head was turn'd perforce away,
And I saw a boat appear.

The Pilot and the Pilot's boy,
I heard them coming fast:
Dear Lord in Heaven! it was a joy
The dead men could not blast.

I saw a third—I heard his voice:
It is the Hermit good!
He singeth loud his godly hymns
That he makes in the wood.
He'll shrieve my soul, he'll wash away
The Albatross's blood.

PART VII

"This Hermit good lives in that wood
Which slopes down to the sea.
How loudly his sweet voice he rears!
He loves to talk with marineres
That come from a far countree.

He kneels at morn, and noon, and eve—
He hath a cushion plump.
It is the moss that wholly hides
The rotted old oak-stump.

The skiff-boat near'd: I heard them talk,
'Why, this is strange, I trow!
Where are those lights so many and fair,
That signal made but now?'

'Strange, by my faith!' the Hermit said—
'And they answer'd not our cheer!
The planks look warp'd! and see those sails,
How thin they are and sere!
I never saw aught like to them
Unless perchance it were

Brown skeletons of leaves that lag
My forest-brook along;
When the ivy-tod is heavy with snow,
And the owlet whoops to the wolf below,
That eats the she-wolf's young.'

'Dear Lord! it hath a fiendish look—
(The Pilot made reply)
I am a-fear'd'—'Push on, push on!'
Said the Hermit cheerily.

The boat came closer to the ship,
But I nor spake nor stirr'd;
The boat came close beneath the ship,
And straight a sound was heard.

Under the water it rumbled on
Still louder and more dread:
It reach'd the ship, it split the bay;
The ship went down like lead.

Stunn'd by that loud and dreadful sound,
Which sky and ocean smote,
Like one that hath been seven days drown'd
My body lay afloat;
But swift as dreams, myself I found
Within the Pilot's boat.

Upon the whirl, where sank the ship,
The boat spun round and round;
And all was still, save that the hill
Was telling of the sound.

I moved my lips—the Pilot shriek'd
And fell down in a fit;
The holy Hermit raised his eyes,
And pray'd where he did sit.

I took the oars: the Pilot's boy,
Who now doth crazy go,
Laugh'd loud and long, and all the while
His eyes went to and fro.
'Ha! ha!' quoth he, 'full plain I see
The Devil knows how to row.'

And now, all in my own countree,
I stood on the firm land!

The Hermit stepp'd forth from the boat,
And scarcely he could stand.

'O shrieve me, shrieve me, holy man!'
The Hermit cross'd his brow.
'Say quick,' quoth he, 'I bid thee say—
What manner of man art thou?'

Forthwith this frame of mine was wrench'd
With a woful agony,
Which forced me to begin my tale;
And then it left me free.

Since then, at an uncertain hour,
That agony returns:
And till my ghastly tale is told,
This heart within me burns.

I pass, like night, from land to land;
I have strange power of speech;
That moment that his face I see,
I know the man that must hear me:
To him my tale I teach.

What loud uproar bursts from that door!
The wedding-guests are there:
But in the garden-bower the bride
And bride-maids singing are:
And hark, the little vesper bell,
Which biddeth me to prayer!

O Wedding-Guest! this soul hath been
Alone on a wide, wide sea:
So lonely 'twas, that God Himself
Scarce seemèd there to be.

O sweeter than the marriage-feast,
'Tis sweeter far to me,
To walk together to the kirk
With a goodly company!—

To walk together to the kirk,
And all together pray,
While each to his great Father bends,
Old men, and babes, and loving friends,
And youths and maidens gay!

Farewell, farewell! but this I tell
To thee, thou Wedding-Guest!
He prayeth well, who loveth well
Both man and bird and beast.

He prayeth best, who loveth best
All things both great and small;
For the dear God who loveth us,
He made and loveth all."

The Mariner, whose eye is bright,
Whose beard with age is hoar,
Is gone: and now the Wedding-Guest
Turn'd from the bridegroom's door.

He went like one that hath been stunn'd,
And is of sense forlorn:
A sadder and a wiser man
He rose the morrow morn.

Black-Eyed Susan

JOHN GAY

All in the Downs the fleet was moored,
　The streamers waving in the wind,
When black-eyed Susan came aboard:
　"O! where shall I my true-love find?
Tell me, ye jovial sailors, tell me true
If my sweet William sails among the crew."

William, who high upon the yard
　Rocked with the billow to and fro,
Soon as her well-known voice he heard
　He sighed, and cast his eyes below:
The cord slides swiftly through his glowing hands,
And quick as lightning on the deck he stands.

"O Susan, Susan, lovely dear,
　My vows shall ever true remain;
Let me kiss off that falling tear;
　We only part to meet again.
Change as ye list, ye winds; my heart shall be
The faithful compass that still points to thee.

"Believe not what the landmen say
　Who tempt with doubts thy constant mind:
They'll tell thee, sailors, when away,
　In every port a mistress find:
Yes, yes, believe them when they tell thee so,
For thou art present whereso'er I go."

The boatswain gave the dreadful word,
　The sails their swelling bosom spread,
No longer must she stay aboard;
　They kissed, she sighed, he hung his head.
Her lessening boat unwilling rows to land;
"Adieu!" she cries; and waved her lily hand.

Spider

PADRAIC COLUM

Spider, Sir Spider,
You're a wonderful fellow—
On a thread I can spy there
You fall and you stop;
You come down with a scurry
And then you go up
In as much of a hurry!
O Spider, Sir Spider,
All brown and yellow,
On a thread light as air,
Where you fall and you stop,
You're a wonderful fellow!

The Night Hunt

THOMAS MacDONAGH

In the morning, in the dark
When the stars begin to blunt,
By the wall of Barna Park
Dogs I heard and saw them hunt.
All the parish dogs were there,
All the dogs for miles around,
Teeming up behind a hare,
In the dark, without a sound.

How I heard I scarce can tell—
'Twas a patter in the grass—
And I did not see them well
Come across the dark and pass;
Yet I saw them and I knew
Spearman's dog and Spellman's dog
And, beside my own dog too,
Leamy's from the Island Bog.

In the morning when the sun
Burnished all the green to gorse,
I went out to take a run
Round the bog upon my horse;
And my dog that had been sleeping
In the heat beside the door
Left his yawning and went leaping
On a hundred yards before.

Through the village street we passed—
Not a dog there raised a snout—
Through the street and out at last
On the white bog road and out
Over Barna Park full pace,

Over to the silver stream,
Horse and dog in happy race,
Rider between thought and dream.

By the stream at Leamy's house,
Lay a dog—my pace I curbed—
But our coming did not rouse
Him from drowsing undisturbed;
And my dog, as unaware
Of the other, dropped beside
And went running by me there
With my horse's slackened stride.

Yet by something, by a twitch
Of the sleeper's eye, a look
From the runner, something which
Little chords of feeling shook,
I was conscious that a thought
Shuddered through the silent deep
Of a secret—I had caught
Something I had known in sleep.

The Diverting History
of John Gilpin

SHOWING HOW HE WENT FARTHER THAN
HE INTENDED AND CAME SAFE HOME AGAIN

WILLIAM COWPER

John Gilpin was a citizen
   Of credit and renown,
A train-band captain eke was he
   Of famous London Town.

John Gilpin's spouse said to her dear,
   "Though wedded we have been
These twice ten tedious years, yet we
   No holiday have seen.

"Tomorrow is our wedding-day,
   And we will then repair
Unto the Bell at Edmonton,
   All in a chaise and pair.

"My sister, and my sister's child,
   Myself, and children three,
Will fill the chaise; so you must ride
   On horseback after we."

He soon replied, "I do admire
   Of womankind but one,
And you are she, my dearest dear,
   Therefore it shall be done.

"I am a linen-draper bold,
   As all the world doth know,

And my good friend the calender,
    Will lend his horse to go."

Quoth Mrs. Gilpin, "That's well said;
    And for that wine is dear,
We will be furnished with our own,
    Which is both bright and clear."

John Gilpin kissed his loving wife;
    O'erjoyed was he to find
That, though on pleasure she was bent,
    She had a frugal mind.

The morning came, the chaise was brought,
    But yet was not allowed
To drive up to the door, lest all
    Should say that she was proud.

So three doors off the chaise was stayed,
    Where they did all get in,
Six precious souls, and all agog
    To dash through thick and thin.

Smack went the whip, round went the wheels,
    Were never folk so glad,
The stones did rattle underneath,
    As if Cheapside were mad.

John Gilpin, at his horse's side,
    Seized fast the flowing mane,
And up he got, in haste to ride,
    But soon came down again;

For saddle-tree scarce reached had he,
    His journey to begin,
When, turning round his head, he saw
    Three customers come in.

So down he came; for loss of time,
   Although it grieved him sore,
Yet loss of pence, full well he knew,
   Would trouble him much more.

'Twas long before the customers
   Were suited to their mind,
When Betty screaming came downstairs,
   "The wine is left behind!"

"Good lack!" quoth he, "Yet bring it me,
   My leathern belt likewise,
In which I bear my trusty sword
   When I do exercise."

Now Mistress Gilpin, (careful soul!)
   Had two stone bottles found,
To hold the liquor that she loved,
   And keep it safe and sound.

Each bottle had a curling ear,
   Through which the belt he drew,
And hung a bottle on each side,
   To make his balance true.

Then over all, that he might be
   Equipped from top to toe,
His long red cloak, well brushed and neat,
   He manfully did throw.

Now see him mounted once again
   Upon his nimble steed,
Full slowly pacing o'er the stones,
   With caution and good heed.

But finding soon a smoother road
  Beneath his well-shod feet,
The snorting beast began to trot,
  Which galled him in his seat.

So, "Fair and softly," John he cried,
  But John he cried in vain;
That trot became a gallop soon,
  In spite of curb and rein.

So stooping down, as needs he must
  Who cannot sit upright,
He grasped the mane with both his hands,
  And eke with all his might.

His horse, who never in that sort
  Had handled been before,
What thing upon his back had got
  Did wonder more and more.

Away went Gilpin, neck or nought;
  Away went hat and wig;
He little dreamt, when he set out,
  Of running such a rig.

The wind did blow, the cloak did fly,
  Like streamer long and gay,
Till loop and button failing both,
  At last it flew away.

Then might all people well discern
  The bottles he had slung;
A bottle swinging at each side,
  As hath been said or sung.

The dogs did bark, the children screamed,
    Up flew the windows all;
And every soul cried out, "Well done!"
    As loud as he could bawl.

Away went Gilpin—who but he?
    His fame soon spread around,
"He carries weight!" "He rides a race!"
    " 'Tis for a thousand pound!"

And still as fast as he drew near,
    'Twas wonderful to view
How in a trice the turnpike men
    Their gates wide open threw.

And now, as he went bowing down
    His reeking head full low,
The bottles twain behind his back
    Were shattered at a blow.

Down ran the wine into the road,
    Most piteous to be seen,
Which made his horse's flanks to smoke
    As they had basted been.

But still he seemed to carry weight,
    With leathern girdle braced;
For all might see the bottle necks
    Still dangling at his waist.

Thus all through merry Islington
    These gambols he did play,
Until he came unto the Wash
    Of Edmonton so gay;

And there he threw the Wash about
  On both sides of the way,
Just like unto a trundling mop,
  Or a wild goose at play.

At Edmonton his loving wife
  From the balcony spied
Her tender husband, wondering much
  To see how he did ride.

"Stop, stop, John Gilpin!—Here's the house!"
  They all at once did cry;
"The dinner waits, and we are tired;"—
  Said Gilpin, "So am I!"

But yet his horse was not a whit
  Inclined to tarry there;
For why? his owner had a house
  Full ten miles off, at Ware.

So like an arrow swift he flew,
  Shot by an archer strong;
So did he fly—which brings me to
  The middle of my song.

Away went Gilpin, out of breath,
  And sore against his will,
Till, at his friend the calender's,
  His horse at last stood still.

The calender, amazed to see
  His neighbour in such trim,
Laid down his pipe, flew to the gate,
  And thus accosted him:

"What news? what news? your tidings tell;
    Tell me you must and shall—
Say, why bareheaded you are come,
    Or why you come at all?"

Now Gilpin had a pleasant wit,
    And loved a timely joke;
And thus, unto the calender,
    In merry guise he spoke:

"I came because your horse would come;
    And, if I well forebode,
My hat and wig will soon be here,
    They are upon the road."

The calender, right glad to find
    His friend in merry pin,
Returned him not a single word,
    But to the house went in;

Whence straight he came with hat and wig,
    A wig that flow'd behind;
A hat not much the worse for wear,
    Each comely in its kind.

He held them up, and in his turn
    Thus showed his ready wit:
"My head is twice as big as yours,
    They therefore needs must fit.

"But let me scrape the dirt away,
    That hangs upon your face;
And stop and eat, for well you may
    Be in a hungry case."

Said John, "It is my wedding-day,
    And all the world would stare,

If wife should dine at Edmonton,
   And I should dine at Ware."

So, turning to his horse, he said,
   "I am in haste to dine;
'Twas for your pleasure you came here,
   You shall go back for mine."

Ah, luckless speech, and bootless boast!
   For which he paid full dear;
For, while he spake, a braying ass
   Did sing most loud and clear;

Whereat his horse did snort, as he
   Had heard a lion roar,
And galloped off with all his might,
   As he had done before.

Away went Gilpin, and away
   Went Gilpin's hat and wig;
He lost them sooner than at first,
   For why?—they were too big.

Now Mistress Gilpin, when she saw
   Her husband posting down
Into the country far away,
   She pulled out half-a-crown;

And thus unto the youth she said,
   That drove them to the Bell,
"This shall be yours, when you bring back
   My husband safe and well."

The youth did ride, and soon did meet
   John coming back amain;
Whom in a trice he tried to stop,
   By catching at his rein;

But not performing what he meant,
  And gladly would have done,
The frightened horse he frightened more,
  And made him faster run.

Away went Gilpin, and away
  Went postboy at his heels,
The postboy's horse right glad to miss
  The lumbering of the wheels.

Six gentlemen upon the road
  Thus seeing Gilpin fly,
With postboy scampering in the rear,
  They raised the hue and cry:

"Stop thief! stop thief!—a highwayman!"
  Not one of them was mute;
And all and each that passed that way
  Did join in the pursuit.

And now the turnpike gates again
  Flew open in short space;
The toll-men thinking, as before,
  That Gilpin rode a race.

And so he did, and won it too,
  For he got first to town;
Nor stopped till where he had got up
  He did again get down.

Now let us sing. Long live the King!
  And Gilpin, long live he!
And when he next doth ride abroad
  May I be there to see!

An Elegy on the Death of a Mad Dog

OLIVER GOLDSMITH

Good people all, of every sort,
　Give ear unto my song,
And if you find it wondrous short,
　It cannot hold you long.

In Islington there was a man
　Of whom the world might say
That still a godly race he ran
　Whene'er he went to pray.

A kind and gentle heart he had,
　To comfort friends and foes;
The naked every day he clad,
　When he put on his clothes.

And in that town a dog was found,
　As many dogs there be,
Both mongrel, puppy, whelp, and hound,
　And curs of low degree.

This dog and man at first were friends;
　But when a pique began,
The dog, to gain some private ends,
　Went mad, and bit the man.

Around from all the neighbouring streets
　The wond'ring neighbours ran,
And swore the dog had lost his wits,
　To bite so good a man.

The wound it seemed both sore and sad
　　To every Christian eye;
And while they swore the dog was mad,
　　They swore the man would die.

But soon a wonder came to light,
　　That showed the rogues they lied:
The man recovered of the bite—
　　The dog it was that died.

Growltiger's Last Stand

T. S. ELIOT

GROWLTIGER was a Bravo Cat, who lived upon a barge:
In fact he was the roughest cat that ever roamed at large.
From Gravesend up to Oxford he pursued his evil aims,
Rejoicing in his title of "The Terror of the Thames."

His manners and appearance did not calculate to please;
His coat was torn and seedy, he was baggy at the knees;
One ear was somewhat missing, no need to tell you why,
And he scowled upon a hostile world from one forbidding eye.

The cottagers of Rotherhithe knew something of his fame,
At Hammersmith and Putney people shuddered at his name.
They would fortify the hen-house, lock up the silly goose,
When the rumour ran along the shore: GROWLTIGER'S ON THE
LOOSE!

Woe to the weak canary, that fluttered from its cage;
Woe to the pampered Pekinese, that faced Growltiger's rage.
Woe to the bristly Bandicoot, that lurks on foreign ships,
And woe to any cat with whom Growltiger came to grips!

But most to Cats of foreign race his hatred had been vowed;
To Cats of foreign name and race no quarter was allowed.
The Persian and the Siamese regarded him with fear—
Because it was a Siamese had mauled his missing ear.

Now on a peaceful summer night, all nature seemed at play,
The tender moon was shining bright, the barge at Molesey lay.
All in the balmy moonlight it lay rocking on the tide—
And Growltiger was disposed to show his sentimental side.

His bucko mate, GRUMBUSKIN, long since had disappeared,
For to the Bell at Hampton he had gone to wet his beard;
And his bosun, TUMBLEBRUTUS, he too had stol'n away—
In the yard behind the Lion he was prowling for his prey.

In the forepeak of the vessel Growltiger sate alone,
Concentrating his attention on the Lady GRIDDLEBONE.
And his raffish crew were sleeping in their barrels and their
    bunks—
As the Siamese came creeping in their sampans and their junks.

Growltiger had no eye or ear for aught but Griddlebone,
And the Lady seemed enraptured by his manly baritone,
Disposed to relaxation, and awaiting no surprise—
But the moonlight shone reflected from a thousand bright blue
    eyes.

And closer still and closer the sampans circled round,
And yet from all the enemy there was not heard a sound.
The lovers sang their last duet, in danger of their lives—
For the foe was armed with toasting forks and cruel carving
    knives.

Then GILBERT gave the signal to his fierce Mongolian horde;
With a frightful burst of fireworks the Chinks they swarmed
    aboard.
Abandoning their sampans, and their pullaways and junks,
They battened down the hatches on the crew within their bunks.

Then Griddlebone she gave a screech, for she was badly
    skeered;
I am sorry to admit it, but she quickly disappeared.
She probably escaped with ease, I'm sure she was not drowned—
But a serried ring of flashing steel Growltiger did surround.

The ruthless foe pressed forward, in stubborn rank on rank;
Growltiger to his vast surprise was forced to walk the plank.
He who a hundred victims had driven to that drop.
At the end of all his crimes was forced to go ker-flip, ker-flop.

Oh there was joy in Wapping when the news flew through
the land;
At Maidenhead and Henley there was dancing on the strand.
Rats were roasted whole at Brentford, and at Victoria Dock,
And a day of celebration was commanded in Bangkok.

The Cat and the Moon

W. B. YEATS

The cat went here and there
And the moon spun round like a top,
And the nearest kin of the moon,
The creeping cat, looked up.
Black Minnaloushe stared at the moon,
For, wander and wail as he would,
The pure cold light in the sky
Troubled his animal blood.
Minnaloushe runs in the grass
Lifting his delicate feet.
Do you dance, Minnaloushe, do you dance?
When two close kindred meet,
What better than call a dance?
Maybe the moon may learn,
Tired of that courtly fashion,
A new dance turn.
Minnaloushe creeps through the grass
From moonlit place to place,
The sacred moon overhead
Has taken a new phase.
Does Minnaloushe know that his pupils
Will pass from change to change,
And that from round to crescent,
From crescent to round they range?
Minnaloushe creeps through the grass
Alone, important and wise,
And lifts to the changing moon
His changing eyes.

The Raven

EDGAR ALLAN POE

Once upon a midnight dreary, while I pondered, weak and weary,
Over many a quaint and curious volume of forgotten lore,
While I nodded, nearly napping, suddenly there came a tapping,
As of someone gently rapping, rapping at my chamber door.
" 'Tis some visitor," I muttered, "tapping at my chamber door:
  Only this and nothing more."

Ah, distinctly I remember it was in the bleak December,
And each separate dying ember wrought its ghost upon the floor.
Eagerly I wished the morrow; vainly I had sought to borrow
From my books surcease of sorrow—sorrow for the lost Lenore,
For the rare and radiant maiden whom the angels name Lenore:
  Nameless here for evermore.

And the silken, sad, uncertain rustling of each purple curtain
Thrilled me—filled me with fantastic terrors never felt before;
So that now, to still the beating of my heart, I stood repeating,
" 'Tis some visitor entreating entrance at my chamber door,
Some late visitor entreating entrance at my chamber door:
  This it is and nothing more."

Presently my soul grew stronger; hesitating then no longer,
"Sir," said I "or Madam, truly your forgiveness I implore;
But the fact is I was napping, and so gently you came rapping,
And so faintly you came tapping, tapping at my chamber door,
That I scarce was sure I heard you"—here I opened wide the door:
  Darkness there and nothing more.

Deep into that darkness peering, long I stood there wondering,
  fearing,
Doubting, dreaming dreams no mortals ever dared to dream
  before;
But the silence was unbroken, and the stillness gave no token,

And the only words there spoken was the whispered word
 "Lenore?"
This I whispered, and an echo murmured back the word,
 "Lenore":
        Merely this and nothing more.

Back into the chamber turning, all my soul within me burning,
Soon again I heard a tapping somewhat louder than before.
"Surely," said I, "surely that is something at my window lattice;
Let me see, then, what therat is, and this mystery explore;
Let my heart be still a moment and this mystery explore:
        'Tis the wind and nothing more."

Open here I flung the shutter, when, with many a flirt and flutter,
In there stepped a stately Raven of the saintly days of yore.
Not the least obeisance made he; not a minute stopped or stayed
 he;
But, with mien of lord or lady, perched above my chamber door,
Perched upon a bust of Pallas just above my chamber door:
        Perched, and sat, and nothing more.

Then this ebony bird beguiling my sad fancy into smiling
By the grave and stern decorum of the countenance it wore,
"Though thy crest be shorn and shaven, thou," I said, "art
 sure no craven,
Ghastly, grim, and ancient Raven wandering from the Nightly
 shore:
Tell me what thy lordly name is on the Night's Plutonian shore!"
        Quoth the Raven, "Nevermore."

Much I marvelled this ungainly fowl to hear discourse so plainly,
Though its answer little meaning—little relevancy bore;
For we cannot help agreeing that no living human being
Ever yet was blessed with seeing bird above his chamber door—
Bird or beast upon the sculptured bust above his chamber door,
        With such name as "Nevermore."

But the Raven, sitting lonely on the placid bust, spoke only
That one word, as if his soul in that one word he did outpour.
Nothing further then he uttered, not a feather then he fluttered,
Till I scarcely more than muttered, "Other friends have flown
    before;
On the morrow *he* will leave me, as my hopes have flown before."
      Then the bird said, "Nevermore."

Startled at the stillness broken by reply so aptly spoken,
"Doubtless," said I, "what it utters is its only stock and store,
Caught from some unhappy master whom unmerciful disaster
Followed fast and followed faster till his songs one burden bore:
Till the dirges of his hope that melancholy burden bore
      Of 'Never—nevermore.' "

But the Raven still beguiling all my sad soul into smiling,
Straight I wheeled a cushioned seat in front of bird and bust
    and door;
Then, upon the velvet sinking, I betook myself to linking
Fancy unto fancy, thinking what this ominous bird of yore,
What this grim, ungainly, ghastly, gaunt, and ominous bird of
    yore
      Meant in croaking "Nevermore."

This I sat engaged in guessing, but no syllable expressing
To the fowl whose fiery eyes now burned into my bosom's core;
This and more I sat divining, with my head at ease reclining
On the cushion's velvet lining that the lamp-light gloated o'er,
But whose velvet violet lining with the lamp-light gloating o'er
      She shall press, ah, nevermore!

Then, methought, the air grew denser, perfumed from an unseen
    censer
Swung by seraphim whose foot-falls tinkled on the tufted floor.
"Wretch," I cried, "thy God hath lent thee—by these angels he
    hath sent thee

Respite—respite and nepenthe from thy memories of Lenore!
Quaff, oh quaff this kind nepenthe, and forget this lost Lenore!"
  Quoth the Raven, "Nevermore."

"Prophet!" said I, "thing of evil! prophet still, if bird or devil!
Whether Tempter sent or whether tempest tossed thee here
  ashore,
Desolate, yet all undaunted, on this desert land enchanted,
On this home by Horror haunted—tell me truly, I implore:
Is there—*is* there balm in Gilead?—tell me—tell me, I implore!"
  Quoth the Raven, "Nevermore."

"Prophet!" said I, "thing of evil—prophet still, if bird or devil!
By that Heaven that bends above us, by that God we both adore,
Tell this soul with sorrow laden if, within the distant Aidenn,
It shall clasp a sainted maiden whom the angels name Lenore:
Clasp a rare and radiant maiden whom the angels name Lenore!"
  Quoth the Raven, "Nevermore."

"Be that word our sign of parting, bird or fiend!" I shrieked,
  upstarting;
"Get thee back into the tempest and the Night's Plutonian shore!
Leave no black plume as a token of that lie thy soul hath spoken!
Leave my loneliness unbroken! quit the bust above my door!
Take thy beak from out my heart, and take thy form from off my
  door!"
  Quoth the Raven, "Nevermore."

And the Raven, never flitting, still is sitting, still is sitting
On the pallid bust of Pallas just above my chamber door;
And his eyes have all the seeming of a demon's that is dreaming,
And the lamp-light o'er him streaming throws his shadow on the
  floor:
And my soul from out that shadow that lies floating on the floor
  Shall be lifted—nevermore!

The Parrots

WILFRID WILSON GIBSON

Somewhere, somewhen I've seen,
But where or when I'll never know,
Three parrots of shrill green
With crests of shriller scarlet flying
Out of black cedars as the sun was dying
Against cold peaks of snow.

From what forgotten life
Of other worlds I cannot tell
Flashes that screeching strife:
Yet the shrill color and the strident crying
Sing through my blood and set my heart replying
And jangling like a bell.

The Broncho That Would Not Be Broken

VACHEL LINDSAY

A little colt—broncho, loaned to the farm
To be broken in time without fury or harm,
Yet black crows flew past you, shouting alarm,
Calling "Beware," with lugubrious singing . . .
The butterflies there in the bush were romancing,
The smell of the grass caught your soul in a trance,
So why be a-fearing the spurs and the traces,
O broncho that would not be broken of dancing?

You were born with the pride of the lords great and olden
Who danced, through the ages, in corridors golden.
In all the wide farm-place the person most human.
You spoke out so plainly with squealing and capering,
With whinnying, snorting, contorting and prancing,
As you dodged your pursuers, looking askance,
With Greek-footed figures, and Parthenon paces,
O broncho that would not be broken of dancing.

The grasshoppers cheered. "Keep whirling," they said.
The insolent sparrows called from the shed,
"If men will not laugh, make them wish they were dead."
But arch were your thoughts, all malice displacing,
Though the horse-killers came, with snake-whips advancing.
You bantered and cantered away your last chance.
And they scourged you, with Hell in their speech and their faces,
O broncho that would not be broken of dancing.

"Nobody cares for you," rattled the crows,
As you dragged the whole reaper, next day, down the rows.
The three mules held back, yet you danced on your toes.
You pulled like a racer, and kept the mules chasing.
You tangled the harness with bright eyes side-glancing,

While the drunk driver bled you—a pole for a lance—
And the giant mules bit at you—keeping their places,
O broncho that would not be broken of dancing.

In that last afternoon your boyish heart broke.
The hot wind came down like a sledge-hammer stroke.
The blood-sucking flies to a rare feast awoke.
And they searched out your wounds, your death-warrant tracing.
And the merciful men, their religion enhancing,
Stopped the red reaper, to give you a chance.
Then you died on the prairies, and scorned all disgraces,
O broncho that would not be broken of dancing.

The Wall of China

PADRAIC COLUM

Who ever had
Such a whale of a plan
As the Emperor
Chin Shih Huan?

To build a wall
As long as the land,
And as high as a hill
Was what he planned.

The wall he built
Was straight and bent,
Camels and elephants
On top of it went.

But the steps so narrow
Three would pack—
That was to keep
The Tartars back.

Not many Tartars
With bow and arrow
The steps could mount
That were so narrow.

Aladdin

JAMES RUSSELL LOWELL

When I was a beggarly boy,
   And lived in a cellar damp,
   I had not a friend nor a toy,
   But I had Aladdin's lamp;
When I could not sleep for the cold,
   I had fire enough in my brain,
   And builded, with roofs of gold,
   My beautiful castles in Spain!

My Lost Youth

HENRY WADSWORTH LONGFELLOW

Often I think of the beautiful town
  That is seated by the sea;
Often in thought go up and down
The pleasant streets of that dear old town,
  And my youth comes back to me,
    And a verse of a Lapland song
    Is haunting my memory still:
    "A boy's will is the wind's will,
And the thoughts of youth are long, long thoughts."

I can see the shadowy lines of its trees,
  And catch, in sudden gleams,
The sheen of the far-surrounding seas,
And islands that were Hesperides
  Of all my boyish dreams.
    And the burden of that old song,
    It murmurs and whispers still:
    "A boy's will is the wind's will,
And the thoughts of youth are long, long thoughts."

I remember the black wharves and the slips,
  And the sea-tides tossing free;
And Spanish sailors with bearded lips,
And the beauty and mystery of the ships,
  And the magic of the sea.
    And the voice of that wayward song
    Is singing and saying still:
    "A boy's will is the wind's will,
And the thoughts of youth are long, long thoughts."

I remember the bulwarks by the shore,
   And the fort upon the hill;
The sunrise gun, with its hollow roar,
The drum-beat repeated o'er and o'er,
   And the bugle wild and shrill.
      And the music of that old song
      Throbs in my memory still:
      "A boy's will is the wind's will,
And the thoughts of youth are long, long thoughts."

I remember the sea-fight far away,
   How it thundered o'er the tide!
And the dead captains, as they lay
In their graves, o'erlooking the tranquil bay,
   Where they in battle died.
      And the sound of that mournful song
      Goes through me with a thrill:
      "A boy's will is the wind's will,
And the thoughts of youth are long, long thoughts."

I can see the breezy dome of groves,
   The shadows of Deering's Woods;
And the friendships old, and the early loves
Come back with a Sabbath sound, as of doves
   In quiet neighbourhoods.
      And the verse of that sweet old song
      It flutters and murmurs still:
      "A boy's will is the wind's will,
And the thoughts of youth are long, long thoughts."

I remember the gleams and glooms that dart
   Across the school-boy's brain;
The song and the silence in the heart,

That in part are prophecies, and in part
　Are longings wild and vain.
　　And the voice of that fitful song
　　Sings on, and is never still:
　　"A boy's will is the wind's will,
And the thoughts of youth are long, long thoughts."

There are things of which I may not speak;
　There are dreams that cannot die;
There are thoughts that make the strong heart weak,
And bring a pallor into the cheek,
　And a mist before the eye.
　　And the words of that fatal song
　　Come over me like a chill:
　　"A boy's will is the wind's will,
And the thoughts of youth are long, long thoughts."

Strange to me now are the forms I meet
　When I visit the dear old town;
But the native air is pure and sweet,
And the trees that o'ershadow each well-known street,
　As they balance up and down,
　　Are singing the beautiful song,
　　Are sighing and whispering still:
　　"A boy's will is the wind's will,
And the thoughts of youth are long, long thoughts."

And Deering's Woods are fresh and fair,
　And with joy that is almost pain
My heart goes back to wander there,
And among the dreams of the days that were,
　I find my lost youth again.
　　And the strange and beautiful song,
　　The groves are repeating it still:
　　"A boy's will is the wind's will,
And the thoughts of youth are long, long thoughts."

The Poplar Field

WILLIAM COWPER

The poplars are felled, farewell to the shade
And the whispering sound of the cool colonnade,
The winds play no longer and sing in the leaves,
Nor Ouse on his bosom their image receives.

Twelve years have elapsed since I first took a view
Of my favourite field, and the bank where they grew;
And now in the grass behold they are laid,
And the tree is my seat that once lent me a shade!

The blackbird has fled to another retreat,
Where the hazels afford him a screen from the heat,
And the scene where his melody charmed me before
Resounds with his sweet-flowing ditty no more.

My fugitive years are all hasting away,
And I must ere long lie as lowly as they,
With a turf on my breast, and a stone at my head,
Ere another such grove shall arise in its stead.

'Tis a sight to engage me, if anything can,
To muse on the perishing pleasures of man;
Though his life be a dream, his enjoyments, I see,
Have a being less durable even than he.

The Lake Isle of Innisfree

W. B. YEATS

I will arise and go now, and go to Innisfree,
And a small cabin build there, of clay and wattles made:
Nine bean-rows will I have there, a hive for the honeybee,
And live alone in the bee-loud glade.

And I shall have some peace there, for peace comes dropping
    slow,
Dropping from the veils of the morning to where the cricket sings;
There midnight's all a glimmer, and noon a purple glow,
And evening full of the linnet's wings.

I will arise and go now, for always night and day
I hear lake water lapping with low sounds by the shore;
While I stand on the roadway, or on the pavements grey,
I hear it in the deep heart's core.

The Fairies

WILLIAM ALLINGHAM

Up the airy mountain,
  Down the rushy glen,
We daren't go a-hunting
  For fear of little men;
Wee folk, good folk,
  Trooping all together;
Green jacket, red cap,
  And white owl's feather!

Down along the rocky shore
  Some make their home—
They live on crispy pancakes
  Of yellow tide-foam;
Some in the reeds
  Of the black mountain lake,
With frogs for their watch-dogs,
  All night awake.

High on the hill-top
  The old King sits;
He is now so old and grey
  He's nigh lost his wits.
With a bridge of white mist
  Columbkill he crosses,
On his stately journeys
  From Slieveleague to Rosses;
Or going up with music
  On cold starry nights,
To sup with the Queen
  Of the gay Northern Lights.

They stole little Bridget
   For seven years long;
When she came down again
   Her friends were all gone.
They took her lightly back,
   Between the night and morrow;
They thought that she was fast asleep,
   But she was dead with sorrow.
They have kept her ever since
   Deep within the lake,
On a bed of flag-leaves,
   Watching till she wake.

By the craggy hill-side,
   Through the mosses bare,
They have planted thorn-trees
   For pleasure here and there.
Is any man so daring
   As dig one up in spite,
He shall find their sharpest thorns
   In his bed at night.

Up the airy mountain,
   Down the rushy glen,
We daren't go a-hunting
   For fear of little men;
Wee folk, good folk,
   Trooping all together;
Green jacket, red cap,
   And white owl's feather!

The Rainbow

WILLIAM WORDSWORTH

My heart leaps up when I behold
   A rainbow in the sky;
So it was when my life began;
So is it now I am a man;
So be it when I shall grow old.
   Or let me die!
The Child is father of the Man;
And I could wish my days to be
Bound each to each by natural piety.

The Solitary Reaper

WILLIAM WORDSWORTH

Behold her, single in the field,
  Yon solitary Highland Lass!
Reaping and singing by herself;
  Stop here, or gently pass!
Alone she cuts and binds the grain,
And sings a melancholy strain;
O listen! for the Vale profound
Is overflowing with the sound.

No Nightingale did ever chaunt
  More welcome notes to weary bands
Of travellers in some shady haunt,
  Among Arabian sands:
A voice so thrilling ne'er was heard
In spring-time from the Cuckoo-bird,
Breaking the silence of the seas
Among the farthest Hebrides.

Will no one tell me what she sings?—
  Perhaps the plaintive numbers flow
For old, unhappy, far-off things,
  And battles long ago:
Or is it some more humble lay,
Familiar matter of to-day?
Some natural sorrow, loss, or pain,
That has been, and may be again?

Whate'er the theme, the Maiden sang
   As if her song could have no ending;
I saw her singing at her work,
   And o'er the sickle bending;—
I listened, motionless and still;
And, as I mounted up the hill,
The music in my heart I bore,
Long after it was heard no more.

The Bells of Shandon

FRANCIS MAHONY

With deep affection,
And recollection,
I often think of
   Those Shandon bells,
Whose sounds so wild would,
In the days of childhood,
Fling around my cradle
   Their magic spells.

On this I ponder
Where'er I wander,
And thus grow fonder,
   Sweet Cork, of thee;
With thy bells of Shandon,
That sound so grand on
The pleasant waters
   Of the River Lee.

I've heard bells chiming
Full many a clime in,
Tolling sublime in
   Cathedral shrine,
While at a glib rate
Brass tongues would vibrate—
But all their music
   Spoke naught like thine;
For memory, dwelling
On each proud swelling
Of the belfry knelling
   Its bold notes free,
Made the bells of Shandon
Sound far more grand on

The pleasant waters
  Of the River Lee.

I've heard bells tolling
Old Adrian's Mole in,
Their thunder rolling
  From the Vatican,
And cymbals glorious
Swinging uproarious
In the gorgeous turrets
  Of Notre Dame;
But thy sounds were sweeter
Than the dome of Peter
Flings o'er the Tiber,
  Pealing solemnly—
O, the bells of Shandon
Sound far more grand on
The pleasant waters
  Of the River Lee.

There's a bell in Moscow,
While on tower and kiosk O!
In Saint Sophia
  The Turksman gets,
And loud in air
Calls men to prayer
From the tapering summits
  Of tall minarets.
Such empty phantom
I freely grant them;
But there's an anthem
  More dear to me,—
'Tis the bells of Shandon,
That sound so grand on
The pleasant waters
  Of the River Lee.

To Autumn

JOHN KEATS

Season of mists and mellow fruitfulness,
　　Close bosom-friend of the maturing sun;
Conspiring with him how to load and bless
　　With fruit the vines that round the thatch-eaves run;
To bend with apples the mossed cottage-trees,
　　And fill all fruit with ripeness to the core;
　　　　To swell the gourd, and plump the hazel shells
With a sweet kernel; to set budding more,
　　And still more, later flowers for the bees,
　　Until they think warm days will never cease,
　　　　For Summer has o'er-brimmed their clammy cells.

Who hath not seen thee oft amid thy store?
　　Sometimes whoever seeks abroad may find
Thee sitting careless on a granary floor,
　　Thy hair soft-lifted by the winnowing wind;
Or on a half-reap'd furrow sound asleep,
　　Drowsed with the fume of poppies, while thy hook
　　　　Spares the next swath and all its twined flowers:
And sometimes like a gleaner thou dost keep
　　Steady thy laden head across a brook;
　　Or by a cider-press, with patient look,
　　　　Thou watchest the last oozings hours by hours.

Where are the songs of Spring? Ay, where are they?
  Think not of them, thou hast thy music too,—
While barred clouds bloom the soft-dying day,
  And touch the stubble-plains with rosy hue;
Then in a wailful choir the small gnats mourn
  Among the river sallows, borne aloft
    Or sinking as the light wind lives or dies;
And full-grown lambs loud bleat from hilly bourn;
  Hedge-crickets sing; and now with treble soft
  The red-breast whistles from a garden-croft;
    And gathering swallows twitter in the skies.

little tree

e. e. cummings

little tree
little silent Christmas tree
you are so little
you are more like a flower

who found you in the green forest
and were you very sorry to come away?
see   i will comfort you
because you smell so sweetly

i will kiss your cool bark
and hug you safe and tight
just as your mother would,
only don't be afraid

look   the spangles
that sleep all the year in a dark box
dreaming of being taken out and allowed to shine,
the balls the chains red and gold the fluffy threads,

put up your little arms
and i'll give them all to you to hold
every finger shall have its ring
and there won't be a single place dark or unhappy

then when you're quite dressed
you'll stand in the window for everyone to see
and how they'll stare!
oh but you'll be very proud

and my little sister and i will take hands
and looking up at our beautiful tree
we'll dance and sing
"Noel Noel"

When Icicles Hang by the Wall

WILLIAM SHAKESPEARE

When icicles hang by the wall
  And Dick the shepherd blows his nail
And Tom bears logs into the hall
  And milk comes frozen home in pail,
When blood is nipp'd and ways be foul,
Then nightly sings the staring owl,
      Tu-whit; Tu-who,
      a merry note,
While greasy Joan doth keel the pot.

When all aloud the wind doth blow,
  And coughing drowns the parson's saw
And birds sit brooding in the snow
  And Marian's nose looks red and raw,
When roasted crabs hiss in the bowl,
Then nightly sings the staring owl,
      Tu-whit; Tu-who,
      a merry note,
While greasy Joan doth keel the pot.

The Solitude of Alexander Selkirk

WILLIAM COWPER

I am monarch of all I survey,
   My right there is none to dispute,
From the centre all round to the sea
   I am lord of the fowl and the brute.
O Solitude! where are the charms
   That sages have seen in thy face?
Better dwell in the midst of alarms
   Than reign in this horrible place.

I am out of humanity's reach,
   I must finish my journey alone,
Never hear the sweet music of speech,
   I start at the sound of my own.
The beasts that roam over the plain
   My form with indifference see;
They are so unacquainted with man,
   Their tameness is shocking to me.

Society, friendship, and love,
   Divinely bestowed upon man,
O, had I the wings of a dove,
   How soon would I taste you again!
My sorrows I then might assuage
   In the ways of religion and truth,
Might learn from the wisdom of age,
   And be cheered by the sallies of youth.

Religion! what treasure untold
   Resides in that heavenly word!
More precious than silver and gold,
   Or all that this earth can afford.

But the sound of the church-going bell
   These valleys and rocks never heard,
Never sighed at the sound of a knell,
   Or smiled when a sabbath appeared.

Ye winds that have made me your sport,
   Convey to this desolate shore
Some cordial endearing report
   Of a land I shall visit no more.
My friends, do they now and then send
   A wish or a thought after me?
O tell me I yet have a friend,
   Though a friend I am never to see.

How fleet is a glance of the mind!
   Compared with the speed of its flight,
The tempest itself lags behind,
   And the swift-winged arrows of light.
When I think of my own native land,
   In a moment I seem to be there;
But, alas! recollection at hand
   Soon hurries me back to despair.

But the sea-fowl is gone to her nest,
   The beast is laid down in his lair,
Even here is a season of rest,
   And I to my cabin repair.
There's mercy in every place,
   And mercy, encouraging thought!
Gives even affliction a grace,
   And reconciles man to his lot.

Siberia

JAMES CLARENCE MANGAN

In Siberia's wastes
  The ice-wind's breath
Woundeth like the toothèd steel.
Lost Siberia doth reveal
  Only blight and death.

Blight and death alone.
  No Summer shines;
Night is interblent with Day.
In Siberia's wastes, alway
  The blood blackens, the heart pines.

In Siberia's wastes
  No tears are shed,
For they freeze within the brain.
Nought is felt but dullest pain,
  Pain acute, yet dead.

Pain as in a dream,
  When years go by
Funeral-paced, yet fugitive;
When man lives and doth not live,
  Doth not live, nor die.

In Siberia's wastes
  Are sands and rocks.
Nothing blooms of green or soft,
But the snow peaks rise aloft,
  And the gaunt ice-blocks.

And the exile there
  Is one with those;
They are part, and he is part!
For the sands are in his heart,
  And the killing snows.

Therefore in those wastes
  None curse the Czar.
Each man's tongue is cloven by
The north blast, who heweth nigh
  With sharp scimitar.

And such doom each drees,
  Till, hunger-gnawn,
And cold-slain, he at length sinks there;
Yet scarce more a corpse than ere
  His last breath was drawn.

The Blind Boy

COLLEY CIBBER

O say what is that thing called Light,
　　Which I must ne'er enjoy;
What are the blessings of the sight,
　　O tell your poor blind boy!

You talk of wondrous things you see,
　　You say the sun shines bright;
I feel him warm, but how can he
　　Or make it day or night?

My day or night myself I make
　　Whene'er I sleep or play;
And could I ever keep awake
　　With me 'twere always day.

With heavy sighs I often hear
　　You mourn my hapless woe;
But sure with patience I can bear
　　A loss I ne'er can know.

Then let not what I cannot have
　　My cheer of mind destroy:
Whilst thus I sing, I am a king,
　　Although a poor blind boy.

The Balloon

ORIGINALLY *As When a Man*

LORD TENNYSON

As when a man, that sails in a balloon,
  Downlooking sees the solid shining ground
Stream from beneath him in the broad blue noon,
  Tilth, hamlet, mead and mound:

And takes his flags and waves them to the mob,
  That shout below, all faces turned to where
Glows rubylike the far-up crimson globe,
  Filled with a finer air:

So, lifted high, the Poet at his will
  Lets the great world flit from him, seeing all,
Higher thro' secret splendours mounting still,
  Self-poised, nor fears to fall,

Hearing apart the echoes of his fame.
  While I spoke thus, the seedsman, Memory,
Sowed my deep-furrowed thought with many a name,
  Whose glory will not die.

I Wandered Lonely...

WILLIAM WORDSWORTH

I wandered lonely as a cloud
That floats on high o'er vales and hills,
When all at once I saw a crowd,
A host, of golden daffodils;
Beside the lake, beneath the trees,
Fluttering and dancing in the breeze.

Continuous as the stars that shine
And twinkle on the Milky Way,
They stretched in never-ending line
Along the margin of a bay:
Ten thousand saw I at a glance,
Tossing their heads in sprightly dance.

The waves beside them danced, but they
Out-did the sparkling waves in glee:
A poet could not but be gay,
In such a jocund company:
I gazed—and gazed—but little thought
What wealth the show to me had brought:

For oft, when on my couch I lie
In vacant or in pensive mood,
They flash upon that inward eye
Which is the bliss of solitude;
And then my heart with pleasure fills,
And dances with the daffodils.

To a Skylark

PERCY BYSSHE SHELLEY

Hail to thee, blithe spirit!
  Bird thou never wert,
That from heaven, or near it
  Pourest thy full heart
In profuse strains of unpremeditated art.

Higher still and higher
  From the earth thou springest
Like a cloud of fire;
  The blue deep thou wingest,
And singing still dost soar, and soaring ever singest.

In the golden lightning
  Of the sunken sun,
O'er which clouds are brightning,
  Thou dost float and run;
Like an unbodied joy whose race is just begun.

The pale purple even
  Melts around thy flight;
Like a star of heaven,
  In the broad daylight
Thou art unseen, but yet I hear thy shrill delight——

Keen as are the arrows
  Of that silver sphere
Whose intense lamp narrows
  In the white dawn clear,
Until we hardly see, we feel that it is there.

All the earth and air
   With thy voice is loud,
As, when night is bare,
   From one lonely cloud
The moon rains out her beams, and heaven is overflowed.

What thou art we know not;
   What is most like thee?
From rainbow clouds there flow not
   Drops so bright to see,
As from thy presence showers a rain of melody:

Like a poet hidden
   In the light of thought,
Singing hymns unbidden,
   Till the world is wrought
To sympathy with hopes and fears it heeded not:

Like a high-born maiden
   In a palace-tower,
Soothing her love-laden
   Soul in secret hour
With music sweet as love, which overflows her bower:

Like a glow-worm golden
   In a dell of dew,
Scattering unbeholden
   Its aërial hue
Among the flowers and grass which screen it from the view:

Like a rose embowered
   In its own green leaves,
By warm winds deflowered,
   Till the scent it gives
Makes faint with too much sweet these heavy-wingèd thieves:

Sound of vernal showers
　　On the twinkling grass,
Rain-awaken'd flowers,
　　All that ever was
Joyous and clear, and fresh, thy music doth surpass.

Teach us, sprite or bird,
　　What sweet thoughts are thine:
I have never heard
　　Praise of love or wine
That panted forth a flood of rapture so divine.

Chorus Hymeneal,
　　Or triumphal chaunt,
Matched with thine would be all
　　But an empty vaunt,
A thing wherein we feel there is some hidden want.

What objects are the fountains
　　Of thy happy strain?
What fields, or waves, or mountains?
　　What shapes of sky or plain?
What love of thine own kind? what ignorance of pain?

With thy clear keen joyance
　　Languor cannot be:
Shadow of annoyance
　　Never came near thee:
Thou lovest; but ne'er knew love's sad satiety.

Waking or asleep,
　　Thou of death must deem
Things more true and deep
　　Than we mortals dream,
Or how could thy notes flow in such a crystal stream?

We look before and after,
    And pine for what is not:
Our sincerest laughter
    With some pain is fraught;
Our sweetest songs are those that tell of saddest thought.

Yet if we could scorn
    Hate, and pride, and fear;
If we were things born
    Not to shed a tear,
I know not how thy joy we ever should come near.

Better than all measures
    Of delightful sound,
Better than all treasures
    That in books are found,
Thy skill to poet were, thou scorner of the ground!

Teach me half the gladness
    That thy brain must know;
Such harmonious madness
    From my lips would flow,
The world should listen then, as I am listening now.

To a Linnet in a Cage

FRANCIS LEDWIDGE

When Spring is in the fields that stained your wing,
And the blue distance is alive with song,
And finny quiets of the gabbling spring
  Rock lilies red and long,
At dewy daybreak, I will set you free
In ferny turnings of the woodbine lane,
Where faint-voiced echoes leave and cross in glee
  The hilly swollen plain.

In draughty houses you forget your tune,
The modulator of the changing hours,
You want the wide air of the moody noon,
  And the slanting evening showers.
So I will loose you, and your song shall fall
When morn is white upon the dewy pane,
Across my eyelids, and my soul recall
  From worlds of sleeping pain.

Fear No More

WILLIAM SHAKESPEARE

Fear no more the heat o' the sun,
  Nor the furious winter's rages;
Thou thy worldly task hast done,
  Home art gone, and ta'en thy wages:
Golden lads and girls all must,
As chimney-sweepers, come to dust.

Fear no more the frown o' the great;
  Thou art past the tyrant's stroke;
Care no more to clothe and eat;
  To thee the reed is as the oak:
The sceptre, learning, physic, must
All follow this, and come to dust.

Fear no more the lightning-flash,
  Nor the all-dreaded thunder-stone;
Fear not slander, censure rash;
  Thou hast finish'd joy and moan:
All lovers young, all lovers must
Consign to thee, and come to dust.

No exorciser harm thee!
Nor no witchcraft charm thee!
Ghost unlaid forbear thee!
Nothing ill come near thee!
Quiet consummation have;
And renownèd be thy grave!

The Splendour Falls

LORD TENNYSON

The splendour falls on castle walls
  And snowy summits old in story:
The long light shakes across the lakes,
  And the wild cataract leaps in glory.
Blow, bugle, blow, set the wild echoes flying,
Blow, bugle; answer, echoes, dying, dying, dying.

O, hark! O, hear! how thin and clear,
  And thinner, clearer, farther going!
O, sweet and far from cliff and scar
  The horns of Elfland faintly blowing!
Blow, let us hear the purple glens replying:
Blow, bugle; answer, echoes, dying, dying, dying.

O, love, they die in yon rich sky,
  They faint on hill or field or river:
Our echoes roll from soul to soul,
  And grow for ever and for ever.
Blow, bugle, blow, set the wild echoes flying,
And answer, echoes, answer, dying, dying, dying.

The Tiger

WILLIAM BLAKE

Tiger, tiger, burning bright
In the forests of the night,
What immortal hand or eye
Could frame thy fearful symmetry?

In what distant deeps or skies
Burnt the fire of thine eyes
On what wings dare he aspire?
What the hand dare seize the fire?

And what shoulder and what art
Could twist the sinews of thy heart?
And, when thy heart began to beat,
What dread hand and what dread feet?

What the hammer? What the chain?
In what furnace was thy brain?
What the anvil? What dread grasp
Dare its deadly terrors clasp?

When the stars threw down their spears,
And water'd heaven with their tears,
Did He smile His work to see?
Did He who made the lamb make thee?

Tiger, tiger, burning bright
In the forests of the night,
What immortal hand or eye
Dare frame thy fearful symmetry?

The Piper

WILLIAM BLAKE

Piping down the valleys wild,
  Piping songs of pleasant glee,
On a cloud I saw a child,
  And he laughing said to me:

"Pipe a song about a Lamb!"
  So I piped with merry cheer.
"Piper, pipe that song again;"
  So I piped: he wept to hear.

"Drop thy pipe, thy happy pipe;
  Sing thy songs of happy cheer:"
So I sung the same again,
  While he wept with joy to hear.

"Piper, sit thee down and write
  In a book, that all may read."
So he vanish'd from my sight;
  And I pluck'd a hollow reed,

And I made a rural pen,
  And I stain'd the water clear,
And I wrote my happy songs
  Every child may joy to hear.

She Walks in Beauty

LORD BYRON

I

She walks in Beauty, like the night
  Of cloudless climes and starry skies;
And all that's best of dark and bright
  Meet in her aspect and her eyes:
Thus mellowed to that tender light
  Which heaven to gaudy day denies.

II

One shade the more, one ray the less,
  Had half impaired the nameless grace
Which waves in every raven tress,
  Or softly lightens o'er her face;
Where thoughts serenely sweet express,
  How pure, how dear their dwelling-place.

III

And on that cheek, and o'er that brow,
  So soft, so calm, yet eloquent,
The smiles that win, the tints that glow,
  But tell of days in goodness spent,
A mind at peace with all below,
  A heart whose love is innocent!

Rose Aylmer

WALTER SAVAGE LANDOR

Ah what avails the sceptred race,
  Ah what the form divine!
What every virtue, every grace!
  Rose Aylmer, all were thine.

Rose Aylmer, whom these wakeful eyes
  May weep, but never see,
A night of memories and sighs
  I consecrate to thee.

Annabel Lee

EDGAR ALLAN POE

It was many and many a year ago,
   In a kingdom by the sea,
That a maiden there lived whom you may know
   By the name of Annabel Lee;
And this maiden she lived with no other thought
   Than to love and be loved by me.

I was a child and she was a child,
   In this kingdom by the sea,
But we loved with a love that was more than love,
   I and my Annabel Lee;
With a love that the wingèd seraphs in Heaven
   Coveted her and me.

And this was the reason that, long ago,
   In this kingdom by the sea,
A wind blew out of a cloud, chilling
   My beautiful Annabel Lee;
So that her high-born kinsmen came
   And bore her away from me,
To shut her up in a sepulchre
   In this kingdom by the sea.

The angels, not half so happy in heaven,
   Went envying her and me;
Yes, that was the reason (as all men know,
   In this kingdom by the sea)
That the wind came out of the cloud by night,
   Chilling and killing my Annabel Lee.

But our love it was stronger by far than the love
    Of those who were older than we,
    Of many far wiser than we;
And neither the angels in Heaven above,
    Nor the demons down under the sea,
Can ever dissever my soul from the soul
    Of the beautiful Annabel Lee.

For the moon never beams without bringing me dreams
    Of the beautiful Annabel Lee;
And the stars never rise but I feel the bright eyes
    Of the beautiful Annabel Lee;
And so, all the night-tide, I lie down by the side
Of my darling,—my darling,—my life and my bride,
    In her sepulchre there by the sea,
    In her tomb by the sounding sea.

The Night Wind

EMILY BRONTË

In summer's mellow midnight
  A cloudless moon shone through
Our open parlour window,
  And rose-trees wet with dew.

I sat in silent musing;
  The soft wind waved my hair;
It told me heaven was glorious,
  And sleeping earth was fair.

I needed not its breathing
  To bring such thoughts to me;
But still it whispered lowly,
  How dark the woods will be!

"The thick leaves in my murmur
  Are rustling like a dream,
And all their myriad voices
  Instinct with spirit seem."

I said, "Go, gentle singer,
  Thy wooing voice is kind:
But do not think its music
  Has power to reach my mind.

"Play with the scented flower,
  The young tree's supple bough,
And leave my human feelings
  In their own course to flow."

The wanderer would not heed me;
    Its kiss grew warmer still.
"Oh come!" it sighed so sweetly;
    "I'll win thee 'gainst thy will.

"Were we not friends from childhood?
    Have I not loved thee long?
As long as thou, the solemn night,
    Whose silence wakes my song.

"And when thy heart is resting
    Beneath the church-aisle stone,
I shall have time for mourning,
    And thou for being alone."

To Night

JOSEPH BLANCO WHITE

Mysterious Night! when our first parent knew
  Thee from report divine, and heard thy name,
Did he not tremble for this lovely frame,
This glorious canopy of light and blue?
Yet 'neath a curtain of translucent dew,
Bathed in the rays of the great setting flame,
Hesperus with the host of heaven came,
And lo! Creation widened in man's view.
Who could have thought such darkness lay concealed
Within thy beams, O sun! or who could find,
Whilst fly and leaf and insect stood revealed,
That to such countless orbs thou mad'st us blind!
  Why do we then shun death with anxious strife?
  If Light can thus deceive, wherefore not Life?

The Express

STEPHEN SPENDER

After the first powerful plain manifesto
The black statement of pistons, without more fuss
But gliding like a queen, she leaves the station.
Without bowing and with restrained unconcern
She passes the houses which humbly crowd outside,
The gasworks and at last the heavy page
Of death, printed by gravestones in the cemetery.
Beyond the town there lies the open country
Where, gathering speed, she acquires mystery,
The luminous self-possession of ships on ocean.
It is now she begins to sing—at first quite low
Then loud, and at last with a jazzy madness—
The song of her whistle screaming at curves,
Of deafening tunnels, brakes, innumerable bolts.
And always light, aerial, underneath
Goes the elate metre of her wheels.
Steaming through metal landscape on her lines
She plunges new eras of wild happiness
Where speed throws up strange shapes, broad curves
And parallels clean like the steel of guns.
At last, further than Edinburgh or Rome,
Beyond the crest of the world she reaches night
Where only a low streamline brightness
Of phosphorus on the tossing hills is white.
Ah, like a comet through flame she moves entranced
Wrapt in her music no bird song, no, nor bough
Breaking with honey buds, shall ever equal.

Felix Randal

GERARD MANLEY HOPKINS

Felix Randal, the farrier, O he is dead then? my duty all ended,
Who have watched his mould of man, big-boned and hardy-
        handsome
Pining, pining, till time when reason rambled in it and some
Fatal four disorders, flesh'd there, all contended?

Sickness broke him. Impatient he cursed at first, but mended
Being anointed and all; though a heavenlier heart began some
Months earlier, since I had our sweet reprieve and ransom
Tender'd to him. Ah well, God rest him all road ever he offended!

This seeing the sick endears them to us, us too it endears.
My tongue had taught thee comfort, touch had quench'd thy tears,
Thy tears that touch'd my heart, child, Felix, poor Felix Randal;

How far from then forethought of, all thy more boisterous years,
When thou at the random grim forge, powerful amidst peers,
Didst fettle for the great grey drayhorse his bright and battering
        sandal!

Boy with His Hair Cut Short

MURIEL RUKEYSER

Sunday shuts down on this twentieth-century evening.
The El passes. Twilight and bulb define
the brown room, the overstuffed plum sofa,
the boy, and the girl's thin hands above his head.
A neighbor radio sings stocks, news, serenade.

He sits at the table, head down, the young clear neck exposed,
watching the drugstore sign from the tail of his eye;
tattoo, neon, until the eye blears, while his
solicitous tall sister, simple in blue, bending
behind him, cuts his hair with her cheap shears.

The arrow's electric red always reaches its mark,
successful neon! He coughs, impressed by that precision.
His child's forehead, forever protected by his cap,
is bleached against the lamplight as he turns head
and steadies to let the snippets drop.

Erasing the failure of weeks with level fingers,
she sleeks the fine hair, combing: "You'll look fine tomorrow!
You'll surely find something, they can't keep turning you down;
the finest gentleman's not so trim as you!" Smiling, he raises
the adolescent forehead wrinkling ironic now.

He sees his decent suit laid out, new-pressed,
his carfare on the shelf. He lets his head fall, meeting
her earnest hopeless look, seeing the sharp blades splitting,
the darkened room, the impersonal sign, her motion,
the blue vein, bright on her temple, pitifully beating.

Fern Hill

DYLAN THOMAS

Now as I was young and easy under the apple boughs
About the lilting house and happy as the grass was green,
  The night above the dingle starry,
    Time let me hail and climb
  Golden in the heydays of his eyes,
And honoured among wagons I was prince of the apple towns
And once below a time I lordly had the trees and leaves
    Trail with daisies and barley
  Down the rivers of the windfall light.

And as I was green and carefree, famous among the barns
About the happy yard and singing as the farm was home,
  In the sun that is young once only,
    Time let me play and be
  Golden in the mercy of his means,
And green and golden I was huntsman and herdsman, the calves
Sang to my horn, the foxes on the hills barked clear and cold,
    And the sabbath rang slowly
  In the pebbles of the holy streams.

All the sun long it was running, it was lovely, the hay
Fields high as the house, the tunes from the chimneys, it was air
  And playing, lovely and watery
    And fire green as grass.
  And nightly under the simple stars
As I rode to sleep the owls were bearing the farm away,
All the moon long I heard, blessed among stables, the night-jars
  Flying with the ricks, and the horses
    Flashing into the dark.

And then to awake, and the farm, like a wanderer white
With the dew, come back, the cock on his shoulder; it was all
    Shining, it was Adam and maiden,
        The sky gathered again
    And the sun grew round that very day.
So it must have been after the birth of the simple light
In the first, spinning place, the spellbound horses walking warm
    Out of the whinnying green stable
        On to the fields of praise.

And honoured among foxes and pheasants by the gay house
Under the new made clouds and happy as the heart was long,
    In the sun born over and over,
        I ran my heedless ways,
    My wishes raced through the house-high hay
And nothing I cared, at my sky blue trades, that time allows
In all his tuneful turning so few and such morning songs
    Before the children green and golden
        Follow him out of grace.

Nothing I cared, in the lamb white days, that time would take me
Up to the swallow thronged loft by the shadow of my hand,
    In the moon that is always rising,
        Nor that riding to sleep
    I should hear him fly with the high fields
And wake to the farm forever fled from the childless land.
Oh as I was young and easy in the mercy of his means,
    Time held me green and dying
        Though I sang in my chains like the sea.

The Fish and the Man

LEIGH HUNT

The Man says:

You strange, astonished-looking, angle-faced,
   Dreary-mouthed, gaping wretches of the sea,
   Gulping salt-water everlastingly,
Cold-blooded, though with red your blood be graced,
And mute, though dwellers, in the roaring waste;
   And you, all shapes beside, that fishy be,—
   Some round, some flat, some long, all devilry,
Legless, unloving, infamously chaste:—

O scaly, slippery, wet, swift, staring wights,
   What is't ye do? What life lead? eh, dull goggles?
How do ye vary your vile days and nights?
   How pass your Sundays? Are ye still but joggles
In ceaseless wash? Still nought but gapes, and bites,
   And drinks, and stares, diversified with boggles?

The Fish says:

Amazing monster! that, for aught I know,
   With the first sight of thee didst make our race
   For ever stare! O flat and shocking face,
Grimly divided from the breast below!
Thou that on dry land horribly dost go
   With a split body and most ridiculous pace,
   Prong after prong, disgracer of all grace,
Long-useless-finned, haired, upright, unwet, slow!

O breather of unbreathable, sword-sharp air,
   How canst exist? How bear thyself, thou dry
And dreary sloth? What particle canst share
   Of the only blessed life, the watery?
I sometimes see of ye an actual *pair*
   Go by! linked fin by fin! most odiously.

After Apple-Picking

ROBERT FROST

My long two-pointed ladder's sticking through a tree
Toward heaven still,
And there's a barrel that I didn't fill
Beside it, and there may be two or three
Apples I didn't pick upon some bough.
But I am done with apple-picking now.
Essence of winter sleep is on the night,
The scent of apples: I am drowsing off.
I cannot rub the strangeness from my sight
I got from looking through a pane of glass
I skimmed this morning from the drinking trough
And held against the world of hoary grass.
It melted, and I let it fall and break.
But I was well
Upon my way to sleep before it fell,
And I could tell
What form my dreaming was about to take.
Magnified apples appear and disappear,
Stem end and blossom end,
And every fleck of russet showing clear.
My instep arch not only keeps the ache,
It keeps the pressure of a ladder-round.
I feel the ladder sway as the boughs bend.
And I keep hearing from the cellar bin
The rumbling sound
Of load on load of apples coming in.
For I have had too much
Of apple-picking: I am overtired
Of the great harvest I myself desired.
There were ten thousand thousand fruit to touch,
Cherish in hand, lift down, and not let fall.
For all
That struck the earth,

No matter if not bruised or spiked with stubble,
Went surely to the cider-apple heap
As of no worth.
One can see what will trouble
This sleep of mine, whatever sleep it is.
Were he not gone,
The woodchuck could say whether it's like his
Long sleep, as I describe its coming on,
Or just some human sleep.

Danny Murphy

JAMES STEPHENS

He was as old as old could be,
His little eye could hardly see,
His mouth was sunken in between
His nose and chin, and he was lean
And twisted up and withered quite,
So that he couldn't walk aright.

His pipe was always going out,
And then he'd have to search about
In all his pockets, and he'd mow
—O, deary me! and, musha now!—
And then he'd light his pipe, and then
He'd let it go clean out again.

He couldn't dance or jump or run,
Or ever have a bit of fun
Like me and Susan, when we shout
And jump and throw ourselves about:
—But when he laughed, then you could see
He was as young as young could be!

The Puppet Play

PADRAIC COLUM

The Showman comes with his box of dolls
Where the locust trees are drooping flowers,
And he makes his dolls like things alive,
And the children watch the play for hours.

But one's not there where the children crowd
To watch the show in the locust shade—
Where's Tinkling Bells, where's Tinkling Bells?—
She'll miss it all if she's long delayed.

But just as another play begins,
And squeaks are made by the grandest doll,
Here's Tinkling Bells! Here's Tinkling Bells,
A-riding on a donkey foal.

A blue umbrella over her head,
She sits and waves a silver fan
While the children clap and the puppets squeak,
And he beams on them all, the Old Showman.

Seumas Beg

JAMES STEPHENS

A man was sitting underneath a tree
Outside the village; and he asked me what
Name was upon this place; and said that he
Was never here before—He told a lot

Of stories to me too. His nose was flat!
I asked him how it happened, and he said
—The first mate of the Holy Ghost did that
With a marling-spike one day; but he was dead,

And jolly good job too; and he'd have gone
A long way to have killed him—Oh, he had
A gold ring in one ear; the other one
—"Was bit off by a crocodile, bedad!"—

That's what he said. He taught me how to chew!
He was a real nice man! He liked me too!

In the Orchard

JAMES STEPHENS

There was a giant by the Orchard Wall
Peeping about on this side and on that,
And feeling in the trees. He was as tall
As the big apple tree, and twice as fat:
His beard poked out, all bristly-black, and there
Were leaves and gorse and heather in his hair.

He held a blackthorn club in his right hand,
And plunged the other into every tree,
Searching for something—You could stand
Beside him and not reach up to his knee,
So big he was—I trembled lest he should
Come trampling, round-eyed, down to where I stood.

I tried to get away.—But, as I slid
Under a bush, he saw me, and he bent
Down deep at me, and said, *"Where is she hid?"*
I pointed over there, and off he went—

But while he searched, I turned and simply flew
Round by the lilac bushes back to you.

The Wind

PADRAIC COLUM

I saw the wind to-day:
I saw it in the pane
Of glass upon the wall:
A moving thing—'twas like
No bird with widening wing,
No mouse that runs along
The meal-bag under the beam.

I think it like a horse,
All black, with frightening mane,
That springs out of the earth,
And tramples on his way.
I saw it in the glass,
The shaking of a mane
A horse that no one rides.

The Darkling Thrush

THOMAS HARDY

I leant upon a coppice gate
  When Frost was spectre-gray,
And Winter's dregs made desolate
  The weakening eye of day.
The tangled bine-stems scored the sky
  Like strings of broken lyres,
And all mankind that haunted nigh
  Had sought their household fires.

The land's sharp features seem'd to be
  The Century's corpse outleant,
His crypt the cloudy canopy,
  The wind his death-lament.
The ancient pulse of germ and birth
  Was shrunken hard and dry,
And every spirit upon earth
  Seem'd fervourless as I.

At once a voice arose among
  The bleak twigs overhead
In a full-hearted evensong
  Of joy illimited;
An aged thrush, frail, gaunt, and small,
  In blast-beruffled plume,
Had chosen thus to fling his soul
  Upon the growing gloom.

So little cause for carollings
   Of such ecstatic sound
Was written on terrestrial things
   Afar or nigh around,
That I could think there trembled through
   His happy good-night air
Some blessèd Hope, whereof he knew
   And I was unaware.

NOTES

The Battle of the Baltic THOMAS CAMPBELL

This action is also known as the Battle of Copenhagen. The battle was in 1801, and in the poem a date is given as April. Denmark would have united hers with the Swedish and Russian fleets, but as this would have enabled the three powers to put up a resistance to the British effort to ban the commerce of neutral shipping with Napoleon's empire—the British fleet set out to prevent such union. When it entered the Baltic in March the only fleet they encountered was the Danish. It was under the command of Denmark's Crown Prince. The battle was forced by Nelson who, however, was not in command of the whole British fleet. In reading "The Battle of the Baltic" we have to remember we are reading a celebration by a British poet. The Danish account makes the whole episode questionable. Readers, however, need not consider anything except the poem. They will be impressed by the grandeur of lines that have in them the proud movement of well-led ships: *And their arms along the deep proudly shone* or such a line as that which brings us close to the action: *It was twelve of April morn by the chime*. Such lines as these and others in "The Battle of the Baltic" show that Thomas Campbell had great mastery of verse even if he did not often display it.

The Bells of Shandon FRANCIS MAHONY

Shandon is a parish in the city of Cork in Ireland, and the bells of its church ring over the River Lee. The poet here has done something

The Notes are listed alphabetically according to the titles of the poems, and not in the order in which they appear in the text.

memorable by giving us, without doing it mechanically, the sound and motion of bells, and by combining something nostalgic with something humorous. Like the poet of "The Burial of Sir John Moore," Francis Mahony was a one-poem poet. None of his other poems is at all memorable.

The Burial of Sir John Moore   CHARLES WOLFE

Sir John Moore, an outstanding British general, was killed in a battle with Napoleon's forces in Spain in 1809. By his dying wish he was buried on the ramparts of Corunna, the city where the battle in which he had received his wound was fought. The poem, which seems so close to the battlefield, was actually written a long way from it. "The Burial of Sir John Moore" was published anonymously in a provincial newspaper. It was attributed to several well-known poets of the time. Later, the draft of the poem was found in a drawer in a room of Trinity College, Dublin. This removed all doubts as to the authorship of a poem that was already famous. It was by the Rev. Charles Wolfe. He had written many other poems, but none in the same class as "The Burial of Sir John Moore."

Felix Randal   GERARD MANLEY HOPKINS

The word "farrier" may puzzle a young reader of today: it has the same meaning as "blacksmith." The farrier dealt exclusively with horses and his main business was shoeing them. This poem about the farrier should be compared with Longfellow's poem about the blacksmith. If we do this we will notice that Longfellow fails to give us the din, the blackness, the heavy strokes that are in Hopkins's *grim forge*. Just in one line he gives us the whole operation of nailing the iron on the hoof of the horse: *Didst fettle for the great grey drayhorse his bright and battering sandal.*

Hohenlinden   THOMAS CAMPBELL

This was a battle fought—on a winter's day, be it noted—between the French and Bavarians on one side and the Austrians on the other. The Austrians were under the command of their Archduke John and the French and Bavarians under a very able French general, Moreau. The Austrians—in their ranks were the fiery Huns or Hungarians—were defeated by the French and Bavarians. The Bavarians—before whose city, Munich, the battle was fought—are not mentioned in the poem: the *furious Franks* are the French.

How They Brought the Good News from Ghent to Aix
ROBERT BROWNING

What the good news was isn't told to us, and to readers of today it isn't of any interest. We can make out that a town in the Netherlands was relieved by a particularly gallant ride and that a horse named Roland did splendidly. Robert Browning more than any other poet in English could enter into the spirit of a strenuous ride, and in "How They Brought the Good News" he has been more strenuous and more spirited—more humorous, too—than in any other of his poems about great gallops. And this is really all we have to know about this terribly urgent mission.

Kubla Khan   SAMUEL TAYLOR COLERIDGE

China, then an unknown part of the world, was visited in the middle of the thirteenth century by a Venetian traveler, Marco Polo. For centuries afterwards China was known in Europe by the name he learned there—Cathay. Its Emperor at the time was Kubla Khan, a descendant of the great Tartar conqueror, Genghis Khan. He had been Emperor for forty-five years and was a very old man when Marco Polo visited him in his capital which was named Kanbalu. Where Xanadu was is not known. Cathay was a land of wonders to the Europeans of the time: amongst the Emperor's possessions that the Venetian traveler noted was a herd of one thousand milk-white horses.

On First Looking into Chapman's Homer   JOHN KEATS

Chapman, a contemporary of Shakespeare, put parts of the Iliad into English verse. *Loud and bold* well describes the style of his translation. The reader of this sonnet should note how the idea of dimension, of spaciousness, goes through it all. Homer is *deep-browed; realms, states, kingdoms, a planet* are brought before us; finally, the greatest of the oceans is before us and we are on a peak in a new world.

On the Loss of the Royal George   WILLIAM COWPER

In 1782 an old ship, the *Royal George*, sank in harbor while undergoing repairs. The circumstances were extraordinary, for although the ship was not seaworthy the crew with the admiral, Kempenfelt, was aboard with many visitors. When we compare this poem with its mournful cadence with the ballad of John Gilpin so cheery in its versification, we realize what a versatile poet William Cowper was.

The Oracles A. E. HOUSMAN

In the fifth century before our era a great Persian army set out to conquer the Greek states. The oracles that were supposed to reveal supernatural knowledge were asked by several of the Greek states whether they should resist an army that far outnumbered any force they could command. The answer the oracles made gave no encouragement. Disregarding their answers, Athens and Sparta went to battle against the Persian invaders. *The Spartans on the sea-wet rock sat down and combed their hair.* This means that, while they awaited the onslaught of the Persians at Thermopylae, they behaved like civilized people, as they would on any other day.

The Solitude of Alexander Selkirk WILLIAM COWPER

Everyone has heard the name of Robinson Crusoe, but hardly anyone has heard the name of the sailor on whose solitary life in a small unvisited island that famous story is based. He was Alexander Selkirk. After a quarrel with his shipmates he asked to be put off on an island that a long voyage had brought them to. He was the sort of man that no one regrets parting company with, and his mates did as he requested. They put him on the uninhabited island of Juan Fernández with some supplies. He begged to be taken back, but the ship's company had no compunction about leaving him as the one human being on an otherwise uninhabited island. For over four years he lived a life that was "out of humanity's reach." In January, 1709, he was taken off by a ship that had chanced on the island, and became a seaman again. Settling on land he wrote an account of his life in Juan Fernández. This became the basis of the great Robinson Crusoe story written by Daniel Defoe.

The Time of the Barmacides JAMES CLARENCE MANGAN

The Barmacides were a family who for some generations served the Caliphs or rulers of Baghdad. In the *Arabian Nights* one of them, Ja'far or Giafar, appears as the companion and adviser of the Caliph Harun al-Rashid. However, Harun turned against him and had Ja'far and all his relatives murdered or imprisoned. This was about A.D. 800. Later, looking back on it, the people of Baghdad saw the period when the Barmacide family gave advisers to the Caliphs as settled and well-ordered. "The time of the Barmacides" became an expression that denoted the golden age of Baghdad.

Tristan da Cunha ROY CAMPBELL

The group of islands called Tristan da Cunha is one of the most isolated places on earth. Alone with a few desolate islets in the South Atlantic, it is nearly two thousand miles from any inhabited place. These islands are volcanic, and were flung up from the depths of the Atlantic Ocean. There are about two hundred and fifty inhabitants, mixed in race but speaking English. Recently some were taken off after a volcanic eruption. They were all evacuated to Britain, but liked Tristan da Cunha's solitude better than the hustle of modern life in Britain, and voted to return. The islands are named for the Portuguese admiral, da Cunha, who was the first to come on them.

Vision of Belshazzar GEORGE GORDON, LORD BYRON

In the tradition that has come to us through the Bible (although this tradition does not agree with the records that have been deciphered in the last hundred years), Belshazzar was the last King of Babylon. The city that was the greatest in the ancient world was captured by the army of the Medes and Persians in the sixth century before our era. According to the tradition the King was feasting in his palace with his great officers (the satraps) when words were written on the wall by a visible hand. The words were only three, but no one known to the King was able to explain them. A former King had made war on the Jewish kingdom, had taken the sacred vessels from the Temple, and had brought a number of Jewish people as captives into the city. One of these captives, Daniel—we know him as Daniel the Prophet—was brought to the Palace; he explained the writing on the wall. The words meant that Belshazzar's kingdom would be taken from him. Soon after, Cyrus, the King of the Medes and Persians, conquered Babylon and liberated the captives.

INDEX OF AUTHORS

INDEX OF FIRST LINES